EAGLE BLUFF
JOURNAL
1895

PHYL MIELKE

In memory of
my husband, Sam,
and in appreciation
of all the help I received
from our family and friends.

THE GREAT LAKES

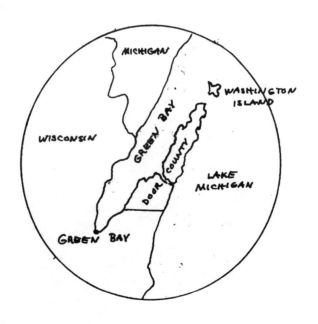

A note from the author

In 1895, a boy named Walter Duclon really was growing up in the Eagle Bluff Lighthouse in Door County, Wisconsin. Walter didn't leave a journal that I know of. I made up this journal. I got the ideas for it from other authors, from copies of real newspaper stories, from talking with old people who remembered what it was like to live without electricity, indoor plumbing and automobiles, and from my imagination. I have combined real people and happenings with imaginary ones in hopes that you will enjoy reading about what a year in Walter's life might have been like. The pictures for this book were done by my son, Jim.

Joseph

Walter   James

Ambrose   Frank   William   Charles

1895

Jan. 1 -- My name is Walter Duclon. I am 12 years old. I live in the Eagle Bluff Lighthouse near Fish Creek, Wisconsin where my father, William Duclon, is the lightkeeper. My mother's name is Julia. I have six older brothers. They are Ambrose, Frank, William, Charles, Joseph and James. Ma gave me this new copy book. She wants me to keep a journal for a year. She said a journal is sort of like Pa's log. I don't have to write in it every day, but I should try to write in it fairly often. I don't think it sounds like much fun, but she's my teacher and she said it would be a good way to practice my writing and spelling and grammar so I guess it's an assignment. She thinks it will be fun to read when I'm a grown man and have children of my own so she said to be sure to explain everything carefully.

Jan. 3 -- It has been real cold and the ice on Green Bay should be getting really thick. Two weeks ago, Pa put out the light for the last time until after the ice melts from the bay in the spring. My brothers are getting ready for ice fishing. They are making a new fish shanty to put out on the ice. It looks like a little house all covered with black

1

tarpaper to keep out the wind and take in the heat from the sun. When it's finished, they will strap it to some metal runners so they can pull it out from shore a ways. Then they will cut a hole in the ice to drop their fishing lines through. My older brothers have been growing beards since fall to protect their faces from the cold. I hope they let me go ice fishing with them this year. Since I'm the youngest, they always treat me like a baby. It's not much fun having six older brothers telling you what to do.

Jan. 8 -- It's cold in the lantern room these days, but Pa spent a good part of today making sure everything up there is in order for the winter. The lantern room is at the very top of the light tower and has ten sides made of cast iron with glass windows on all sides. In the lantern room is the lens that makes the light from the burning wicks inside it bright enough to be seen more than 16 miles away. There are two circular wicks made of cloth that soak up the fuel oil and give off light when they are set on fire. Before a Frenchman named Fresnel invented this lens, light could only be seen about 3 miles out on the water. A Fresnel lens looks a little like a beehive made out of glass prisms. There's an inside row of prisms that magnify the light from the burning wicks and an outside row of prisms that bend the light rays into a strong plane of light. Some lighthouses on ocean coastlines have Fresnel lenses that are twelve feet tall but ours is a third that size. Our tower isn't very tall as lighthouses go, only 43 feet, but that's because we're already on a bluff up off the water 33 feet. The tower is a part of our house so you don't have to go outside to get to the tower. We get from the first floor of our house up to our bedroom by going into the tower and climbing up the stairs as far as the doorway leading to the second floor. It's a clever design for a lighthouse and the Lighthouse Service has used it time and again across the country. We boys towed the fish shanty out onto the bay today. It was my brother Will and Ruth's first wedding anniversary so they came out here for supper. Their little baby Julia is getting cute.

Jan. 9 -- It's a good thing we put the shanty out yesterday because it snowed about 8 inches last night and it's not very easy going today. Frank showed me how to put a red bead near the hook on my line to attract the fish. We already caught some nice trout. There are a lot of other shanties on the bay. Some are as big as 5 feet by 7 feet and have a bed and a table and a stove in them. The men live in them all week and then strap metal creepers on their feet for walking across the ice to shore on the weeekend so they can spend Sunday with their families and get fuel for their stoves and food for another week. Fish buyers come by the shanties with big sleds every few days to pick up the fish.

Jan. 12 -- Joe and I skied into town today to go sledding down the big hill. That's what everyone calls the road coming into Fish Creek from the south. It's about 4 miles from our lighthouse to town but it was worth the trouble. With all the snow, we really got some good rides, almost down to the water. It being Saturday, all the town boys were there. Some of the older ones were hitching their sleds to the horse drawn sleighs as they went through town. There is too much snow on the bay for ice boating or skating, but it sure was perfect for sledding downhill in town.

Jan. 13 -- The men are starting to mark a road across Green Bay to Marinette. They line up

Christmas trees and other evergreen branches. It is about 18 miles straight across from Fish Creek. Some people use covered sleds with stoves inside to make the trip. I saw some sail sleighs out today too. Those are really big ice boats that are used for transporting lumber and shipments of fish. Since they are powered by wind, they can go a lot faster than regular sleighs that are pulled by horses.

Jan. 14 -- It was really cold and windy today and the snow blew around something fierce. After I finished my lessons with Ma, I practiced on my guitar for a couple of hours. Maybe if I get real good, my brothers will let me play in their band. We had a nice evening at home tonight. Ma was working on another crazy quilt. She uses scraps of real fancy material like velvet and satin, and embroiders around the edges of each piece with different stitches. The scraps aren't put together in an orderly manner like most quilts. That's why it's called a crazy quilt. Ma's known for her crazy quilts. She has given each of my brothers' wives and children a new quilt of their very own. Charlie fetched in some snow and Ma made snow candy for us. She just boils some brown sugar and water together for a while and then we spoon it over some snow in a dish. It's real good.

Jan. 16 -- After the big wind, there are big patches of ice on the bay that are nearly clear of snow. We strapped our skate blades on over our boots and skated clear into town and back. The only bad thing is that our skates keep coming loose and you have to stop all the time to tighten them up so they don't come off and send you crashing down. Will and Charlie are going to get out the iceboats one of these days. They won't let me take one out alone, but maybe I'll get to ride with one of them.

Jan. 19 -- Pa left this morning for Sturgeon Bay. He is going on land in Roy Thorp's covered sleigh. I hope they have plenty of buffalo robes and bear skins in it. In order not to overwork the horses, they'll take two days to get there. They will have to stay overnight in Egg Harbor, both going and coming home. They will stay at Roy's Uncle Levi's big white house with the cupola on top. Pa told me to be sure to keep enough firewood in the house. With four stoves to keep going, I really have to keep hauling. And since I'm the youngest, and I'm not off fishing like my brothers, it's my responsibility. Of course, if we don't get any company, Ma probably won't want the stove in the parlor lit. We close the parlor doors and we don't even go in there unless company comes. She has her fancy furniture in there and likes to keep that room just so. We mostly stay in the dining room and the music room during the winter. We have a stove in our bedroom upstairs for when it's real cold. None of my friends have stoves in their upstairs bedrooms. They just have grates in the bedroom floors where the heat from downstairs can rise up to heat the upstairs rooms. I guess we're lucky. Since Ammie and Will each got married and moved into their own places, there's only five of us boys sharing the upstairs bedroom instead of seven.

Jan. 20 -- Pa is still down in Sturgeon Bay but we had a good time last night with Ma. She was telling us how she and Pa met. His first lightkeeping assignment was on Mackinac Island, Michigan, as an assistant to her Pa, Ambrose Davenport, who was the head lightkeeper. My oldest brother is named after him. Grandma Davenport was half Chippewa Indian so that makes me and my brothers

7

part Indian. Ma and Pa got married on Mackinac and that is where their second baby, Albert, is buried. Pa was transferred to Beaver Island before I was born. We moved to Eagle Bluff Lighthouse in Wisconsin when I was just one year old.

Jan. 21 -- Tonight the boys let me practice with them for a square dance they're going to play at on Friday night. They said I have really improved and maybe one of these days they'll let me play at a dance with them. I'm going to work on my guitar every day. Ma said she was pleased with how this journal is going. She helped me correct my spelling and grammar mistakes. Pa still isn't home, but we aren't expecting him for at least two more days.

Jan. 22 -- Today was really an exciting day. Charlie was on his way back to shore from the fish shanty and he was carrying a pretty big catch. He slipped on the ice and fell real funny and broke his leg. At first he thought he had just twisted it, and he limped to shore. It's a good thing Ma always puts a lamp in the music room window when the boys are out ice fishing because they don't have the lighthouse beacon to guide them home in winter.

Charlie's leg kept swelling bigger and bigger and hurt like crazy so Frank took him in the cutter across Eagle Harbor on the ice to Ephraim

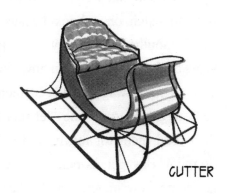

CUTTER

to see Doc Horn. Doc put a cast on it and told Charlie to sit around with his leg up on a chair for a few days. He gets out of doing chores for awhile but he doesn't get to do any fun things either, so I guess I feel sorry for him. He says it really hurts. Ma gave him some tea that she makes out of special herbs she collects and dries. It's an old Indian remedy she learned from her mother and it is supposed to help bones mend. Pa will be surprised when he gets back to find Charlie with a broken leg.

Jan. 24 -- Pa got home safe and sound from Sturgeon Bay. He said fishermen were spearing sturgeon through big holes in the ice and were getting some as big as five feet long. They are big, ugly fish and can weigh up to 150 pounds. They're hard to catch on a hook because they have real funny mouths. That's why they spear them. Some years back, there were so many sturgeon that people used to spear wagon loads of them and take them back to their farms. They let them rot in a pit and then used them for fertilizer. I suppose that's how Sturgeon Bay got its name. Ma was real happy to get some new material and other sewing supplies from Cochem's general store, and Pa brought some fresh oysters from Mann's grocery. He brought a new string for my guitar too so maybe that will help me play even better.

Jan.25-- Pa made his famous oyster stew for supper today and we had a whole houseful of folks here to help eat it. He doesn't skimp on the oysters or the cream. After the stew, we had scalloped oysters with bacon on top along with celery and pickles and rolls. We had apples and Ma's butterscotch caramels for dessert, if we had room. I can hardly move.

Jan. 28 -- Today is Monday so Ma washed clothes. She washes clothes on Monday no matter what the weather. I guess that's because we take our baths on Saturday night and change our clothes on Sunday. I have to carry water in from the cistern pump on Sunday night and put it in the clothes boiler on the stove so it can begin to warm up overnight. I'm glad the cistern is buried right outside the kitchen door. We have to keep a hole in the ice down by the crib dock to get our drinking water out of, and carrying buckets of water up all those icy steps in winter isn't easy. At least we can get the wash water right out of the cistern. Rain and melting snow from the roof runs down the rain pipes and collects in the cistern. Ma does her washing in the kitchen in winter. She boils the white clothes in the boiler. Then she ladles the water into the washtub where she scrubs the clothes on a washboard with a bar of yellow soap. She keeps adding hot water from the boiler and uses a peggy stick to stir the clothes around and then to lift them out of the hot water. After they are rinsed, she hangs them outside - even if they freeze. She says they dry a little by freezing and it makes the white clothes stay whiter. It looks pretty silly to see long flannel drawers and shirts and pants hanging on a line, stiff as boards. And it gets pretty cold hanging

11

the clothes out, that's for sure. They usually don't get dry outside in winter and sometimes they are still stiff as boards when we bring them in, so we stand them around the kitchen until they thaw enough to put over a rack near the stove. It's good no one usually comes visiting on Mondays or they would see our underwear standing around the kitchen.

Jan. 29 -- Since I wrote about washing yesterday, I'll write about ironing today. Just like Ma washes every Monday, she irons every Tuesday. First thing in the morning she has to dampen the good clothes by dipping her fingers in a pan of water and shaking drops of water on the clothes. One by one she rolls them up tight and wraps them together in a towel to sit for a few hours. She has a long ironing board with cloths wrapped around it for padding and she puts it on top of the dining room table. She keeps two sad irons heating on the stove there so that when one gets too cool she can switch to the other, and back and forth like that. Jim and I went sledding on the road going down to Lighthouse Bay. We got some good rides.

Jan. 31 -- Today is Jim's 15th birthday. Ma made his favorite supper, corned beef and cabbage, and apple dumplings for dessert. This being the end of my first month of journal keeping, I will include some news from the last Door County Advocate. That's our weekly newspaper. Grover Cleveland is President of the United States, but a lot of people don't like him, it seems. A humane society for the prevention of cruelty to human beings and animals was organized in Sturgeon Bay with Frank Long elected president. The Plum Island lighthouse is getting a steam fog signal. I hope we never get a fog signal. Pa says they blast your ears out. Some lighthouses have a bell but we don't even have that. A new schooner named the Finnland is being built at Mud Bay north of Baileys Harbor. Ma says I'm doing a real good job with this journal and I like writing in it more than I thought I would.

Feb. 3 -- We took the sleigh into town yesterday to watch ice harvesting in the harbor. One of the men has a horse drawn ice saw but other men were cutting the blocks of ice with two-man saws. The loose blocks of ice are floated over to where they are loaded on big sleighs to be hauled off to the ice houses. We boys had fun riding back and forth on the sleighs. In the ice houses, sawdust from the mills is spread between the layers of ice blocks so they aren't all stuck together come summer. Fish Creek is starting to get summer visitors from as far away as Milwaukee and Chicago and even some from St. Louis and those folks are used to having ice to cool their food and drinks. They'll be harvesting ice for about three weeks but when they are done, the harbor usually freezes over real smooth where they've cut out the ice and it turns into a great skating pond. The skaters keep it shoveled clear of new snow and at night they build a bonfire right in the middle of the harbor.

Feb. 4 -- There was a story in Saturday's Advocate about a train wreck near Forestville on the Ahnapee and Western Railroad. The engine derailed and went down an embankment and a fire started. They were able to put it out right away and no passengers were seriously injured and the freight came through all right. They just built the railroad from Ahnapee to Sturgeon Bay last year. It took three boatloads of rails from Buffalo, New York to build it. This first winter has been a bad one for the new railroad. Snow piles up in the cuts and the engine has to try to lunge through the drifts. One time, the cab windows even shattered when the train hit a big drift. They've had to shut down the line a couple of times because of snow. Some drifts were seven feet deep after one storm. Ed Kenyon is the engineer and he says old engine #1 is no match for northeast Wisconsin winters.

Feb. 6 -- Today is Ammie's 26th birthday. He and Ada Belle live in Fish Creek with their two little boys so we all went there for supper. They are thinking of moving to Washington Island where Ada came from. I just did my usual chores today. I always have the animals to feed. We have a horse named Queenie, a cow named Dixie, and some chickens. I have to milk Dixie twice a day and shovel out the manure. Our dog's name is Jack and we have four cats too. Jack is good at chasing up game, and Joe and Frank have killed a good lot of squirrels and rabbits this winter. They're all skinned and dressed and hanging in the summer kitchen alongside the fish. Whatever Ma doesn't cook fresh keeps frozen out there. We don't use the summer kitchen for anything but storage in the winter.

THE BARN

Sometimes I go along hunting with them, but I haven't hit anything yet and I don't have a gun of my own.

Feb. 9 -- Aunt Jo brought out a big bunch of feathers from her geese and ducks. She's not really my aunt but we call some of our favorite grownups Aunt and Uncle. Some of her children came along and we all sat around the table and stripped feathers. It's pretty tiring just pulling the down off the quills, but we had a good time anyway. Ma says she can always use a new pillow or feather tick. While we were stripping feathers, we took turns cranking the ice cream freezer. To make ice cream, you first have to break up a piece of ice by putting it in a gunny sack and hitting at it with a shovel. While one of the boys was outside doing that, Ma cooked up a batch of custard from cream and eggs and sugar and vanilla. The custard goes in a can in the center of the freezer, and paddles are fastened to the inside of the can's lid. There's a crank sticking out so you can make the paddles stir the custard. The ice and salt are put in layers around the can in the freezer. Then you crank away to keep stirring the custard and as the ice melts, the custard is turning to ice cream. You know when it's ready because it gets too hard to turn the crank any more. Boy does it taste good.

Feb. 13 -- We're in the middle of a real cold spell. The Advocate said the thermometer registered 31 below one day last week. I also read that Squire Jackson of Baileys Harbor escaped serious injury Friday after the lighted pipe he placed in his overcoat pocket ignited as he walked along the street in Sturgeon Bay. That must have given him a little warmth. Ma had me working down cellar today breaking sprouts off the potatoes. I can't say that's a job I get any pleasure out of. Milton Hanson is a good friend of Charlie's and we just heard that his Pa died. I sure feel bad for him. I guess I'll go to bed early tonight. It still gets dark early and the more we burn the oil lamps, the more soot there is to clean out of the lamp chimneys come Saturday.

Feb. 14 -- It's St. Valentines Day today. Someone doesn't get into Fish Creek every day to pick up the mail, but Charlie asked Frank to be sure to pick it up today. The mail comes up from Sturgeon Bay in a big bob sleigh that has a cab on it big enough for the driver and a small stove. The bags of mail are stacked in a box at the rear of the sleigh and covered by a heavy tarpaulin. Charlie was hoping for a Valentine from Edith Gehrke. He's kind of sweet on her, even if she is still learning English and talks with a German accent. She's all right, I guess, and she sure can play the piano. He didn't get a Valentine from her.

Feb. 16 -- Today was Charlie's turn to have a birthday. He is 19 years old now. He can hobble around some on his leg but he still couldn't get out to have any real fun. He was sure happy when five of his friends, including Edith Gehrke, came out to see him. They were real impressed with the schooner he's carving. He tried his hand at carving because it was so boring to just sit around. Now it seems he has found himself a new hobby. Edith really liked our rosewood piano. It's not a regular baby grand piano. Maybe seven or eight years ago, Ma and Pa saw a regular one advertised for fifty dollars by the Chickering Company in the east. That included the shipping cost so they ordered one. It came all the way out here, by boat of course, and it took all the older boys and some of their friends to get it unloaded at the Lighthouse Bay pier and hauled up the road on the wagon to the lighthouse. Then they found out it wouldn't fit through any of the doors in the lighthouse so it had to go back to Boston. It turns out the piano company also makes a baby grand that has a shorter keyboard and removable legs, so they shipped one of those out instead. With the legs off, it just fit through the door. We've all learned to play it at least a little. I used to have to screw the stool way up as high as it would go but now I'm almost as tall as Jim.

Between us all, we play quite a few instruments. Besides the piano and guitar, we have two violins, a cello, an accordion, and a stand-up bass. Some of the older boys are learning to play horns, too. Ma and Pa have always liked music and wanted us all to be able to play. They helped us all get started but then we mostly taught ourselves. At first we just played together at home to entertain ourselves, but now my older brothers have this band and they play at dances real often and even get paid sometimes. If they are going to play someplace where there's no piano, they can take the legs off ours and load it on the wagon or on the sleigh if it's winter. They wrap it in some of Ma's older quilts and off they go. They've even been known to play all night. I haven't practiced my guitar much lately. I better get working on it if I want them to let me play in their band.

Feb. 17 -- Today was perfect for ice boating and a bunch of the older boys were racing to Chambers Island and back. After they were tired of racing, Will took me out for a ride. It's scary at times, because you go real fast, but it's lots of fun and Will let me handle the sheet rope that adjusts the mainsail.

Feb. 23 -- Will is 21 years old today. He and Frank are in the fishing business together and operate out of Shanty Bay just north of here where Ole Larson has his cabin. Ole was one of the earliest white men in these parts and settled first on Eagle Island with his wife. When he ran out of trees on the island to cut for fuel for passing steamers, he took his cabin apart, made a raft out of the logs, floated it to the mainland and rebuilt the cabin. The fish boats are all hauled out there at Shanty Bay for the winter but the boys will catch plenty of trout and herring using gill nets. They make holes in the ice and then run the nets under the ice from hole to hole using long running poles. Right before Christmas they caught so many fish they even got their names in the Advocate. Ma fixed boiled fish for supper tonight. She wraps a big trout or whitefish in a fresh napkin and boils it in a long pan along with two handfuls of salt. Then she lifts the fish out of the water onto a platter and carefully takes away the napkin and the skin and bones. Then she pours a cup or more of melted butter over the fish. We always have boiled potatoes and sweet-sour beets with boiled fish. It's one of my favorite meals.

Feb. 28 -- February sure went fast. Ma and I went over my journal again and she said to keep up the good work. I couldn't find much news of interest in the Advocate this week. They've put a postal car on the train so mail from Chicago and Milwaukee will reach Sturgeon Bay a lot faster. There's an engine house shaped kind of like part of a circle, and a turntable that was moved up from Ahnapee. Now they're working on a depot that will even have a telephone in it. They probably won't build tracks north of Sturgeon Bay. A peninsula is better suited to boat transportation than railroad, I guess. I sure would like to ride on a train someday but it costs $1.95 just to go to Green Bay.

Mar. 2 -- Ma got Frank to take her into Fish Creek to a quilting bee today. They could still go over the ice, but one of these days it won't be safe any more. The road into town will be thawing soon

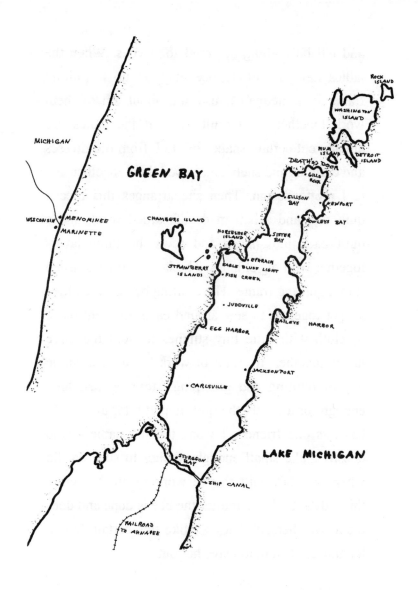

MICHIGAN

WISCONSIN • MENOMINEE
• MARINETTE

GREEN BAY

CHAMBERS ISLAND

ROCK
ISLAND

WASHINGTON
ISLAND

RUM
ISLAND

DETROIT
ISLAND

DEATH'S DOOR

GILLS
ROCK

ELLISON
BAY

NEWPORT

ROWLEYS BAY

HORSESHOE
ISLAND

SISTER
BAY

STRAWBERRY
ISLANDS

EPHRAIM

EAGLE BLUFF LIGHT

• FISH CREEK

• JUDDVILLE

EGG HARBOR

• BAILEYS HARBOR

• JACKSONPORT

• CARLSVILLE

LAKE MICHIGAN

• STURGEON
BAY

SHIP CANAL

RAILROAD
TO AHNAPEE

DOOR COUNTY, WISCONSIN

23

and it'll be nothing but mud for weeks. When the ladies have a quilting bee they set up a quilting frame in someone's house and about ten of them work together on a quilt. One of the ladies has already cut certain shapes of cloth from old dresses and curtains and such, and sewed them together in a real pretty design. Then she arranges this pieced quilt top, and a batt made of carded wool, and a quilt back into layers and sews the three layers together with big stitches. The ladies all help fasten it to a quilting frame. The quilting bee is when they all get together to sew around each different piece of cloth with little tiny stitches to hold the three layers together. It's a lot of work but after a whole day of quilting and gossiping, stopping just long enough for a lunch, the quilt is pretty far along. Ma has this one friend - I won't tell her name - who doesn't make small enough stitches to suit Ma. So when it's Ma's quilt they're working on, Ma takes this lady's stitches out after the bee is done and does them over herself. They all like this certain lady a lot and don't want to leave her out.

Mar. 11 -- I read in Saturday's Advocate that there are some big cracks in the ice so anyone out fishing or crossing the bay to Michigan should be very watchful. It also said that some men in the US. Congress were talking about impeaching President Cleveland. I asked Ma what that meant and she told me to look it up in our dictionary. It means to charge the President with misconduct in public office, but I'm not sure what that means either.

Mar. 13 -- We keep having birthdays in the family. Today Joe is 17. He shot a deer yesterday so we had roast venison, red cabbage and mashed potatoes for his birthday supper. Since the forest was all cut over for timber and fuel some years back, the trees are all young and the underbrush is thick. It's easier to spot a deer this time of year than when everything is all leafed out. Joe asked for Ma's special applesauce cake for dessert.

Mar. 16 -- I finally have something exciting to write about. We've been hearing the ice cracking the last few days. It makes a really loud noise. A big crack opened up straight out from the lighthouse and a fisherman from Ephraim was stranded on the other side. We could see him and the open water from the upstairs window. Will, Frank and Walter

Chambers went out to rescue him. They have this sled with a boat on it that they can pull out over the ice. When they got to the crack, they launched the boat into the water and fetched the stranded man back across to solid ice. Nary a spring goes by without someone getting stranded on the bay. About five years ago, Anton Olson and Anton Amundson were on an ice flow when it broke loose and they floated from near Chambers Island way up to Ellison Bay. They were on the flow all night. When it bumped into Whaleback shoal, they climbed off onto the shoal. They were stuck there for two nights before someone got out to rescue them.

Mar. 19 -- We heard about Constable Billy Dingman's accident on the bay yesterday. He and Mrs. Dingman were out on his sail sleigh and ran into a crack and were thrown off the sleigh. Lucky they weren't hurt. The bay can be dangerous this time of the year. Ma had me scub out the privy today. I sure don't like that job.

Mar. 20 -- Besides working on my lessons like always, I churned butter for Ma today. She had saved up quite a lot of top cream. You just have to make the dasher go up and down until the lumps of butter separate out. After she adds some salt, Ma puts it in her butter press to squeeze out the rest of the buttermilk, and the butter comes out in a nice firm block. I'll never forget the time when I was little and accidentally broke her churn. I hid on the window ledge in the cellar hoping no one would find me out. Ma didn't get too mad at me. My brothers went into town tonight to hear Doctor Hale lecture at the Gibraltar town hall. Charlie is out and about now that his cast is off so he went too. Doc Hale and his wife sell some stuff called Kickapoo Indian Remedy. Ma says it's no Indian remedy. She says it'll just make you drunk. But they put on quite a show so no one wants to miss it. Doc always carries a $1000 bill to impress people with. I wonder if it is real. That means I was home alone with Ma and Pa. I got out the stereoscope and looked at pictures of the Yosemite Valley, the Garden of the Gods, Flowers of the Rocky Mountains and Fishing for Salmon. When you look through a stereoscope, you're looking at two pictures but you see only one and everything in the picture stands out like statues. Maybe I'll get to hear Doc Hale next year when he's up this way again.

THE PRIVY

Mar. 22 -- Charlie, Joe and Jim are all off to a surprise birthday party for Gertie Gessler tonight. Seems like I'm not old enough to do anything yet. This afternoon Jim and I drilled holes in the maple trees around our place and put the spiles in the holes so the sap can run out into the buckets underneath. It takes warm days and cool nights to get the sap running good. Each day, I'll collect all the sap and when I'm done collecting it, Ma will boil it down for hours until it's just right for syrup. You have to boil down about 40 gallons of sap to get just one gallon of syrup. The bottles of syrup will get stored down cellar along with all the other food there. It's good we have a cellar under the whole house because we need it to store all our food including the milk and eggs I take down there every day.

Mar. 27 -- Today is Pa's 50th birthday so everyone came for supper. Ammie's and Will's families are staying overnight so even the grandchildren got to stay up late. Pa told us again how he watched the battle of the Monitor and the Merrimac from shore during the Civil War. Those were two of the first iron clad warships in the world. The Confederates had the Merrimac and the Union had the Monitor. Dad was a soldier in the 14th Regiment of the Union Army at the time. Neither ship really won the battle, because neither side had invented shells that could pierce an iron hull. Later, Pa was wounded at Gettysburg and finished the war in a hospital. Pa likes to tell stories and he is a lot of fun. Everyone outside the family calls him Captain because he usually puts his lightkeeper uniform on every day after he's caught up on his sleep and his lightkeeping chores. Ma has to make his uniform according to very special directions. The coat is double breasted and has five big brass buttons on each side of the front and two small buttons on each sleeve. It has two hip pockets and two inside pockets. The vest is single breasted and has three pockets and five buttons. His cap has a visor, a yellow metal chin strap, and a Lighthouse Service badge on the front. Ma says he looks dashing in his uniform. I suppose she means he's handsome.

Mar. 31 -- The end of another month already. The winter months when the light is out are fun because there is less work for everyone. But now, we're all kind of looking forward to spring, even if it means more work. Yesterday's Advocate said that Ed Morton bought Lundberg's store in Fish Creek and Alex Lundberg is going to reopen his store in Juddville. Otto Anderson will be glad to hear that. With his seventeen children to keep fed, I'm sure he'll be happy to have a store handy. The Advocate warned that the road to Sturgeon Bay where it goes through Plum Bottom Station is a quagmire. It was also in the paper that Captain Ezra B. and Jenny Goodman were holding a dance for fishermen and sailors in Bailey's Harbor next week. I don't suppose I can call myself either yet.

THE SUMMER KITCHEN

Apr. 1 -- This was Ma's first washday out in the summer kitchen this spring. One day last week I helped her scrub it out after the winter. She'll keep

doing the cooking in the house until it gets too hot
to heat up the cook stove in here, but she'll do her
washing out in the summer kitchen from now until
late fall. Along with the big stove and the wash
bench for the rinse tubs, there's a hand cranked
washing machine out there that takes some of the
work out for Ma but gives me an extra chore.
Instead of just stirring the clothes around in a tub
with the peggy stick, Ma can put the clothes and hot
water and shaved soap in the washing machine and
when I turn the handle, a thing called an agitator
stirs the clothes around to get them clean. Then
there's a thing called a wringer that cranks too, and
when you feed the clothes through it one at a time,
it squeezes the water out of them. From there they
go into a rinse tub, then they get wrung out again
into another rinse tub, put through the wringer one
more time and then hung on the washline. Ma puts
a washline up in the summer kitchen if it's raining.
She doesn't want the washing machine in the house
kitchen in winter because it takes up too much
room. When the weather warms up a little more,
we'll start taking our baths in the summer kitchen
too. It used to be that I got to use the bath water

first, being the youngest, but now it's pretty much first come, first served.

Apr. 2 -- Ma is really going at the spring housecleaning. First thing today Jim and I took the four stove pipes outside so we could knock all the soot from winter out of them. Then we took up all the rugs but the parlor carpeting and hung them on a line. It is my job to hit at them with the carpet beater until no more dust or dirt comes out. While the rugs were on the line, Ma scrubbed the floors and mop boards. Since the parlor carpeting is tacked down, it'll have to wait until we get a little fresh snow. We're sure to get at least one last snowfall. Then I'll bring some snow in and spread it on the carpeting and Ma will sweep it around to pick up the dirt. Then I have to get the dirty snow swept up into the dustpan and back outside before it melts. Ma won't rest until she's washed every wall, floor, curtain, dish and window in the place. In the meantime, Pa's up in the tower getting everything shined up for the season. He keeps all his linens and other cleaning supplies in our one closet which is off the upstairs hall. Lamp wicks go in there too. He has special rags and polishes for the brass, and for the glass and for the wood. We boys have been taking turns painting sections of the metal stairway up to the lantern room. There are 55 steps from the cellar to the lantern deck. We paint every other step first so we can still get up the stairway to our room and Pa can get up to the light. I really hate painting but when you live in a lighthouse, you do a lot of painting. The Service sends us enough paint every year to cover every surface and we are expected to use it all up. It used to be we could choose between red, green and other colors but now most everything has to be gray or white. The paint comes powdered and we mix it with oil for the wood and metal parts and with water for the walls. The worst part is scrubbing everything before you can paint it. Even if it's not a time to be doing our regular painting chores, Pa will find a painting job for anyone who gets in trouble and has a punishment coming.

Apr. 5 -- Since we don't have enough land around the lighthouse to raise food for our animals, our neighbors the Sorensons always give us some hay and some grain and corn in exchange for helping with the harvesting. We get our straw for bedding from them too. Today I went over there to help them pick stones out of the fields. They have a stone boat that's pulled by a horse. It's kind of like a big wooden sled without runners. Everyone walks along beside it and loads it with stones that have been pushed up to the surface by the frost. Then we have to unload all the stones along the edge of the field. Each year the stone fences get a little higher from all the new stones that appear in spring. Seems there's never an end to picking stones in Door County.

Apr. 6 -- The ice is still pretty solid on the bay. I went out today and cut Ma some pussy willows and some balsam poplar. The pussy willows don't go in water or they'll get blossoms but the poplar branches go in water so the buds will open up and give off that good smell. The first little hepatica flowers will soon be showing up in the woods and the ducks and geese are stopping by the marsh inland from Weborg's point on their way north . Ma and Pa and Frank went into Fish Creek last night for the annual Gibraltar Township meeting. I guess Oscar Hale made a pretty big speech about how hard times are right now. Then everyone voted to limit the town clerk's salary to $75 a year and the assessor's to $50. Health Officer Myron Stevens gets $10. L.L.Hill was elected to a one year term as town chairman. They voted to give up to $5 a month from the poor fund to any family that needs temporary help.

Apr. 9 -- The ice is starting to break up. Now we need a heavy south wind to clear the bay. Eagle Bluff Light was built here in 1868 because ships were having a lot of trouble navigating this part of Green Bay. They have to either stay between the shore and the three little Strawberry Islands or go clear around Chambers Island in order to avoid the shoals. When a boat is sailing between our shore and the Strawberries, it's so close we can call out to it with our megaphone. That's a cone-shaped thing usually used by dock masters to direct boats coming into port. The boats have megaphones too so we can carry on a regular conversation. Our light also helps boats find the Horseshoe Island harbor. It's supposed to be the safest harbor on the Great Lakes with four way protection from the wind, counting the mainland bluff. It's shaped just like a horseshoe. The water in the harbor is deep enough for even large boats to tie up to trees on the island. A few years back though, late in the fall, the big steamer the City of Ludington took shelter at Horseshoe and tied up to a tree. The Captain didn't set a watch and the tree was uprooted by the strain of the wind on the boat, and the boat drifted clear into Shanty Bay and couldn't be freed until spring.

Apr. 13 -- Tonight Pa lit the light for the first time this season. This time of year, there's about 13 hours between sunset and sunrise. He has to put more oil in the lamp every eight hours and he has to clean all the prisms every morning after he puts the lamp out. He has to keep the wicks trimmed and the chimney clean too. If the prisms get coated with soot, they won't work right. We boys help with the cleaning sometimes but Pa is pretty fussy about how it's done. We mostly just help clean the soot off the lantern room windows. It's still cold up there this time of year and late fall is even colder. Before the lighthouses were built in Door County, many ships went down and a lot of lives were lost. Pa's job is very important and he knows it. He'll be on the job every night from now until late December. I don't know if I want to be a light keeper or not. Maybe I'll join my brothers' fishing crew. I know I like being around water and boats.

Apr. 14 -- Today was a red letter day for me because I got to change from my long flannel underwear into my summer drawers. Being Easter Sunday I drove Ma in to church this morning. She's really a Baptist but since there's no Baptist church around here, we went to the Episcopal church. That church used to be the house of a fisherman named Charlie Gessler but after his wife died, he never did finish building it. About the time we moved here, the Episcopalians bought it and made it into a church shaped like a cross. I'm not much for church, but Gustie Larson was there this morning and I got to talk to her. She asked me if I was going to be at the Easter Ball being held at Jorn's Hall in Bailey's Harbor tomorrow night. Clarke's string band is playing and she's going to go with her parents. Ma and Pa won't be going since the light has to be lit so early these nights and I suppose my brothers won't want me tagging along. Oh well, I can't dance anything but squares anyway, and I'm not too good at them.

Apr. 16 -- The Advocate had a story about another derailment near Nasewaupee. It seems the construction company that was building the railroad last year was more interested in getting a bonus for finishing the job on time than they were in doing the job right. There's an area the train engineers have named the cranberry marsh because the road bed gets flooded over all the time and it's built on such spongy ground that the trains keep derailing. I don't think I would like to be on a train when it went off the tracks into water.

Apr. 20 -- I finally got to do something really fun. I went along with four of my brothers to net smelt last night. We got into town by the creek at about midnight. Everyone must have heard that the smelt were running because the creek banks were crowded. Smelt are little fish that go upstream to spawn every spring. You have to catch them before they swim back into the bay. The men had nets, tubs, baskets and anything else they could use to dip into the water to scoop out the little fish. Some just used their hands. Everyone's got a lantern and it's a real pretty sight. I didn't like the part where I had to bite the head off a smelt from my first netting, but that's what everyone does and I didn't want the others to think I was a sissy. To clean them, you rub them between your hands with coarse salt before you behead and gut them. Ma cooked a mess of them today, first dipping them in batter and then frying them in lard. They are so crispy that you can eat bones and all.

Apr. 25 -- Today was our last family birthday for awhile. Ma was 50 years old today. She came from an even bigger family than ours. Maybe that's how she came to learn to do so many things. Besides sewing most of our clothes and always having a quilt or two in the making, she spins and knits and crochets and tats. She even showed us boys how to tat and crochet. She says it'll come in handy when we're mending nets. Sophia Sjoquist up in Sister Bay keeps a flock of sheep and Ma gets her wool from her.

Apr. 27 -- The Fanny Hart made her first stop of the season in Fish Creek today. The Hart Boat Company owns her and the Harriet, and Hills own the Erie L. Hackley and the Cecelia Hill. They sail all around Green Bay, stopping at all the villages on our side and on the Michigan side. They're called propellers and they have pretty much replaced the side-wheelers. The really big propellers are owned by the Goodrich Line. They make regular runs from Chicago to Mackinac Island and back. They go through the ship canal in Sturgeon Bay and then stop at the towns on both sides of Green Bay. Some of the older Fish Creek boys have taken a fancy to the blond Norwegian girls in Ephraim and they sometimes will ride up to see them on a boat and then walk back home. When a big propeller arrives, half the people in town go down to watch it dock. Their hulls are black and their superstructures are white. The stacks are red and black. The Goodrich flag is white with red letters G.T.Co.and it flies from the foremast while the American flag flies at the stern. It's a sight to see. The captain uses bells, whistles and tweets to signal the engine room when he's docking. I read in the Dock Gossip column in the Advocate that the Goodrich Line has more business than it can handle. Pa says all shipping has really increased since the war between the states because the port cities like Chicago and Milwaukee are growing so big and have need of so much lumber and shingles and cordwood and iron ore and stone, not to mention salted fish.

Apr. 30 -- I have another month of my journal done. I would have liked a journal from my Pa when he was growing up in New York state back in the fifties so maybe my children will be glad I wrote this. The Advocate had a story about how Dale Vorous fell off the dock and got knocked unconscious and Ed Williams rescued him. Ed was so excited, he didn't notice how cold the water was. Another Advocate story said some folks are talking about changing the name of Fish Creek to Claflin. I hope they don't because it was Increase Claflin who named it Fish Creek. He must have liked that name. It was even in the paper about Lenox Hogan joining my brothers' fish crew. I'd hardly call that news but I guess they are the biggest fishing operation in these parts.

May 2 -- Today is Ma and Pa's 28th wedding anniversary. Seems we have a lot of family celebrations in spring. We had a couple of real cold days, but now things are warming up and the trilliums are coming up in the woods. We have this big vegetable garden quite a ways from the house. It's fenced in because of the deer wanting to eat everything. The lighthouse grounds are fenced too but we couldn't put a garden inside that fence because there's not enough top soil near the lighthouse to grow anything. It is on the edge of a rocky limestone bluff and if you try to dig down, you hit bedrock less than a foot down. Ma can grow a few flowers near the house and there are trees and bushes that somehow manage to put their roots down through the cracks in the rock ledge, but it's just not good for a vegetable garden. I carried a load of old manure to the garden site and dug it in. I'd been dumping wood ashes on the garden too so they got dug in at the same time. Pa will be planting greens and peas and onion sets any day now and root vegetables after that. Beans go in a little later and then, when frost isn't likely, he'll put in the plants he's been growing in a flat on the window sill. I hope we don't have a summer as dry as last year because I sure get tired of carrying water from the cistern pump all the way to the garden.

May 6 --Pa went to town for some baby pigs today. They are so cute, I don't like to think of butchering them in the fall. At least the pigs aren't quite so cute when they're grown. If we don't name them, it's easier to butcher them. I rode along to town with Pa and we went up the creek a ways to get some watercress. We had watercress salad for supper tonight with sweet-sour bacon dressing. Ma always breaks up a boiled potato in it so the greens don't bite your tongue so much. About this time of year she fixes dandelion greens the same way.

May 11 -- Jim was driving Ma into town today in the buggy and a black bear came out of the woods right in front of them. Old Queenie bolted and gave them a merry ride until Jim could get her settled down. It's lucky they didn't spill out. I'm still practicing on my guitar every chance I get and Ma makes me keep on with my lessons until the town school lets out. Pa said he heard they are thinking of building a school in Blossomberg. That would be real handy for me, and Ma would probably be glad to stop doing lessons after all these years. It might be kind of fun to go to a regular school.

May 13 -- I looked for some news for my journal in Saturday's Advocate but it was all make believe stories, the kind girls mostly like to read, and advertisements for baking powder and furniture and such. It did say that the Lake Michigan car ferry started its runs between Kewaunee, Wisconsin and Luddington, Michigan. I wish I could watch as they load train cars right into the hull of a boat. It would have to be a pretty big boat. There was another story about how hard it is for schooners to get through the opening in the new railroad bridge across Sturgeon Bay without damaging either the bridge or the boat or both. I wish I could watch that too. It's just about this time in May that the

Inspector arrives so we've all been pretty busy making sure everything is ship shape.

May 15 -- Any time one of us would go past the front window lately, we'd grab the spy glass to see if we could see the Dahlia heading this way. That's the Inspector's tender. Joe just happened to spot it about noon today so we were really prepared. Once before when the Dahlia was spotted, we went like crazy to get everything ready for inspection, and the Inspector went on by. All that work for nothing. Pa's got a lot of citations for having the best lighthouse in the county and he wants to keep up his good record. With twelve other lighthouses, there's plenty of competition. We mostly don't want the Browns at Cana Island to beat us out. Ma said when we were little she would scrub us up before the Inspector docked. Now we boys usually just take ourselves away when he comes. Ma puts on a fresh apron and Pa makes sure his uniform looks proper. The beds all have to be made and the clothes hung up. There's only six hooks in our bedroom. Service regulations, I guess. When I outgrew the cradle downstairs in the music room and moved upstairs to sleep, my clothes went under someone else's until Ammie moved out and I got my own hook. Any extra shoes have to be lined up under the beds with their toes pointing out. Pa always stands at attention and salutes when the Inspector docks. The Inspector is real friendly and doesn't stay very long, but he looks in every corner of the house, the grounds and the lantern room. Since we never know exactly when he is coming, we have to keep everything looking good all the time.

May 16 -- We were talking over the inspection we had yesterday and Pa got out his rule book for me to see. I know about the daily log where he's supposed to write the time at sunset when he lights the lamp and the time at dawn when he puts it out. He's also supposed to log passing ships, wind and weather conditions, the supplies he has used up and visitors to the light. Pa writes when the tenders put the buoys out on Frying Pan shoals and when they take them in. The lightkeeper has to watch the lamp all through the night to be sure it doesn't go out and there can't be any visitors to the lantern room after sunset. During the day, only three people can be in the lantern room at a time and visitors are not allowed to touch the lens. A light keeper must always be sober, orderly, and polite to strangers. If a lightkeeper is caught intoxicated, that means drunk, or his light is not lit when it is supposed to be, he will be dismissed from the Service. There's 34 pages in the rule book just telling how to operate and clean the lamp. At the bottom of each page in his log, Pa writes, "Examined and correct, William Duclon, Keeper."

May 17 -- I just took a look at the new shelf of books the Inspector brought on Wednesday. There's 50 books to a shelf. Every time he comes to inspect, he brings us a new shelf and takes away the old one. I'm going to read Trip to the Moon by Jules Verne first. Some of the books like the Five Little Pepper books are for younger children. I mostly read the ones for grownups now. Ma made her first rhubarb pies of the year. She's going to make a rhubarb upside-down cake next, she said. That is my favorite.

May 25 -- The grounds around the house are real pretty. The lilac bush outside the kitchen door is blooming already and the snowball bush is getting ready to. The fruit trees are in blossom and the forget-me-nots look like blue clouds on the floor of the woods. Everyone in town is shining things up to get ready for the summer visitors. Fish Creek gets livelier every year. There are street lamps on the main corners that different men take turns lighting and putting out each day. The gravel in the streets gets graded every so often so the ruts aren't too deep, and there's plenty of hitching posts in front of the stores. Mail gets brought up from Sturgeon Bay in a wagon with a cab on it to keep out the rain. Of course, Barringers drive their herd of cows through town to pasture every day like always, fancy visitors or no. A Mr. Legler from Milwaukee bought some lots in town last summer and there's talk of a Dr. Welker from Chicago wanting to start a resort. He heard about Fish Creek from a school principal in Chicago who's been spending his summers here for a few years already. A Mr. George Clark has a stove factory in Chicago and he bought some land from Asa Thorp and plans to build a summer home for his family on it. Funny how word spreads. A business visitor likes it here and decides to bring his family along next time. They stay in someone's house and the next thing you know, that house turns into a small hotel. And next after that, the business visitor builds his own house for his family. What with the Goodrich Line making weekly trips up here from Chicago, folks can fill a big trunk with clothes, load it on the steamer, be up here in two days and stay the whole summer. Frank heard that his friend Ted Thorp, who just finished a business course at Eastman College in Poughkeepsie New York, was going to take over managing the Thorp Hotel from his pa. This summer, the hotel will offer a horse and rig to their visitors for taking in the sights. The hotel charges $3.75 a week for each person. Last year they had over one hundred visitors.

May 31 -- Today is Decoration Day so we all had a big time. We had pancakes for breakfast with a special banana topping Ma makes with eggs, sugar, sliced bananas and vanilla. Then we went into town for the parade. Town officials were on horseback and the masons and G.A.R. men marched. The veterans wore their uniforms if they could still get in them. Since Pa was a member of the Grand Army of the Republic he marched with them, and Ma and the other wives of veterans rode in carriages. There were lots of bicycles and pony carts and baby carriages and scooters, and even a goat cart, all decorated with red, white and blue streamers. Anyone who could play a horn or a drum marched in the band and they played The Stars and Stripes Forever and the Washington Post March over and over. After the parade, one of the veterans recited the Gettysburg Address and everyone joined in singing The Battle Hymn of the Republic. We all went to the cemetery at Blossomberg to decorate the graves of relatives with bouquets of snowballs in chipped mason jars. Then everyone had a picnic lunch. Ammie and Will and their families joined in our picnic and a good time was had by all.

Jun. 1 -- Pa was talking about how even though there is a lot more shipping on the Great Lakes these days, there are fewer ships going past our light since the Sturgeon Bay ship canal was dug about fifteen years ago. Before that, there was a narrow swampy stretch of land connecting southern Door County to northern Door County at the east end of Sturgeon Bay. It was almost impossible for land travelers to cross over, but it kept boats from being able to go from Lake Michigan to Green Bay.

The canal that was dug is real narrow. Schooners can't make it through on their own but need to be towed through by steam tugs. Now, boats heading for Green Bay from the south end of Lake Michigan don't have to risk Death's Door and they shorten their route by about 100 miles. There's a lighthouse where the canal meets Lake Michigan and it has a fog signal that can be heard eight miles away. Then there's the Sherwood Point lighthouse where Sturgeon Bay meets Green Bay. It just has a bell that is struck automatically every twelve seconds. It sure must be hard for visitors to these parts to keep straight whether we're talking about bodies of water or towns when our towns all seem to be named after bodies of water.

Jun. 2 -- Death's Door is the passage of water between the tip of the Door County peninsula and Washington Island. I asked Pa how it got its name and he said French voyageurs named it Porte des Mortes, which means Death's Door in French, when they heard the story about a whole band of Indians who were killed by other Indians when they were trying to land after crossing over from the island. Later, Door County was named after the strait. Pa said it's still a good name for that passage because of all the ships that have foundered there due to the tricky winds and currents. There is a lighthouse on Pilot Island in Death's Door and the keeper has made a lot of rescues since it was built. The government has plans to put up range lights on Plum Island as well as a fog signal. Some of those island lighthouses are really isolated and sometimes bad weather makes going to or from the island impossible for weeks at a time. That must be pretty lonely and scary. I'm glad our light is on the mainland and that we have neighbors nearby.

Jun. 3 -- The weather is starting to warm up real nice. Of course, this is the month when we get some bad storms. There was one a few years back when a lot of boats went down and a lot of people were lost. Everyone refers to it as the Alpena storm because the Goodrich steamer the Alpena went down with all hands and passengers lost. The Dahlia reached Horseshoe Island harbor just in time and rode out that storm real good. Our dock at the foot of the steps is no good in rough weather. It's a crib dock which is like a big log crate filled with coarse rocks. It's 37 feet long but the water is only

2 1/2 feet deep alongside so a good sized boat can't get in there. We keep the small rowboat supplied by the Service tied up there but most other boats use our other dock at the bay a quarter mile south of here. Frank and the others keep their fish boats at Shanty Bay not quite a mile north of here. We're seeing more steamers and fewer schooners go by these days. The newest steamers are long and ride real low in the water and are slow moving. They have a pilot house forward and the power plant is aft. They are used for iron ore, coal and grain mostly. They have steel hulls and large propellers and aren't bothered quite so much by storms as the sailing boats.

June 4 -- I just wrote about the storms yesterday, and at 2 o'clock today we got a squall from the southwest that blew some of the blinds right off the house. We all went down cellar during the worst of it. Ma and Pa were real worried about the boys being out fishing but turns out they made it to safe harbor in time. Pa thinks we got at least two inches of rain.

Jun. 7 -- Jim and I spent the whole day painting. As long as some of the blinds were off due to the storm, we gave them all a new coat of green paint. Every summer, the summer kitchen and the barn and the lean-to have to get painted as well as all the trim on the house and the privy. The lighthouse is mostly made of brick from Milwaukee and we don't have to paint the brick. We use white paint on all the outside wood except for the barn which is painted partly buff. Then there's the wood fence that goes around three sides of the lighthouse grounds to paint too. At least we don't have to paint the stone wall along the top of the bluff. With red tin roofs on all the buildings, it does look nice. Jim and I will be crawling into our bed early tonight.

Jun. 9 -- My older brothers got into a fight with the Brown boys last night in Baileys Harbor. Their pa has been the keeper at Cana Island light for about four years and they've been picking fights with us ever since. There's five boys and a girl in that family. I don't know what started the fight but I guess our boys cleaned up on them. Sure wish I could have been there. Ma gets real upset when the boys get into fights with them, but Pa says the

Browns are probably jealous of all the citations he gets.

Jun. 10 -- Today, I had to take everything out of the lean-to by the kitchen door and paint it inside and out. I even had to paint the brick around the door to the kitchen white because that's kind of like an inside wall and all of our inside walls are white.

There are hooks in the lean-to for our coats and for the brass dustpan and the foxtail brush. Pa's cap has a special hook out there too. In winter Ma lets us hang our coats inside behind the kitchen door to keep them warm. Then we keep a supply of dry wood in the lean-to. The yellow lady slippers are in bloom now and they are Ma's favorites so I picked some for her today.

Jun. 11 -- It rained all day today so I painted the parlor walls. There are more things on the wall to bother with in that room like the pictures and the magazine rack and the pipe rack. Why Ma likes those pictures of fruit and of dead fish, I'll never know. Then there's the music box to worry about and the big lamp with the fancy painted globe. I have to cover the flowered carpeting with newspaper and be careful not to get paint on the stove. Ma is really proud of her new sofa in there but I hate sitting on it because the horsehairs in the stuffing come right through the velvet and poke you. Our house is lots nicer than the other houses in this area. Most of them are cabins with only two or three rooms, some with only one room and a loft. Our house has five rooms on the first floor and two on the second floor and a cellar underneath. Being made of brick and all, it's even nicer than most of the houses in town. I don't know anyone else who has a brick privy.

Jun. 12 -- The first hatch of lake flies arrived overnight. They cling to everything, people, animals and buildings. I'm glad all our new paint had a chance to dry before they hatched. A year doesn't go by without at least two hatches of them so I should be used to them by now. They all die after two or three days and then I'll have to sweep them up. At least they don't bite like the deer flies that we usually get in July.

Jun. 14 -- Pa went to town yesterday to get some lumber and since both sawmills are right down by the dock, he took a look at the new boathouses Don Chambers and John Melvin built for the rowboats they rent to the summer visitors. The little boats are real popular already and the men plan to build some more before next summer. It seems pretty silly to me that folks would enjoy rowing around Fish Creek Harbor in a little boat, but I suppose if you come from the city where you can't do that sort of thing, maybe it is kind of fun. The boat that the Service provides for us was designed right here in Door County. Joseph Harris, who was a lightkeeper himself at Dunlap Reef, began designing little rowboats and sailing catboats. The Service inspectors liked the looks of them so much that they ordered a bunch of them for the lightkeepers to use.

Jun. 16 -- It's been pretty quiet around here today. The Browns came to Fish Creek last night and really got even with our boys. Charlie got hurt a little but he said they nearly killed Frank and Will. Ma said that Will should have been home with his wife and child and that Frank was old enough to know better. I guess I'm glad I wasn't there. Frank stayed overnight at Will's so Ma wouldn't see how bad he was hurt. I hope that's the end of the fighting at least for awhile.

Jun. 18 -- The school in Fish Creek closed today so I can stop my lessons too, except for this journal, of course, which really doesn't seem like an assignment any more. Since I've been doing so much painting, Ma let me off pretty easy on my lessons lately. I'll be glad when the painting is finished so I can spend some time with my friends. Before you know it, summer will be over and it will be time to start lessons again. But next year it looks like I'll be going to a regular school because the men are making plans to build one at Blossomberg only about a mile or so from here.

Jun. 21 -- I spent most of the day at Sorenson's making hay. The hay had already been cut and turned over and allowed to dry real good, so today we pitched it onto the wagon and hauled it to the barn. I like working the big fork and ropes and pulleys that they use to get it into the hay mow through the high door at the end of the barn. I brought a wagon load of hay home for our animals. Tonight is the shortest night of the year. Pa will only have to spend about eight and a half hours watching the lamp. Then each night gets longer until the bay freezes over and he can put out the light for the winter.

Jun. 25 -- There was an article in Saturday's Advocate about how a lot of Sturgeon Bay merchants think a new free foot and wagon bridge should be built across the bay. Before the railroad came to Sturgeon Bay, Leathem Smith had already built a wagon bridge with a swingspan to let boats go through. The railroad built up an earthen roadway far out into the bay from the Sawyer side of the bridge and a steam barge brought in a new 90 ton drawbrige. The wagons have to cross the bridge on the railroad tracks and sometimes a wheel slips into the groove in the tracks and gets wrenched right off. Maybe a second bridge would be a good idea. There were a few lines in the paper about my older brothers' fishing operation. It said how they were hook fishing off St. Martins Island now but how they could get home frequently because they have a pretty big sailboat. I'm glad they didn't write anything about the fight with the Browns the week before. Ma would have had a fit. My brothers got over their cuts and bruises all right.

Jun. 26 -- Clouds of grasshoppers are swarming over Door County. They're chewing up the crops and gardens and driving everyone crazy. They aren't so bad here as they are farther south so I guess we are lucky.

Jun. 29 -- Myron Stevens uses his horse drawn grader regularly to keep deep ruts from forming in the Fish Creek streets. This week he's using it to make Main Street into a half mile long race track for Fourth of July. There will be foot races too and lots of other athletic sports, according to the Advocate. I can hardly wait.

Jul. 5 -- Yesterday was one of my favorite holidays. We boys got up about 3:30 to set off some of our fire crackers. We have all different sizes of crackers as well as caps, blanks, sky rockets, snakes, pinwheels and Roman candles. Ma says she hates the fire cracker part of Fourth of July. After breakfast, we went into town for the celebration. Arthur Sutherland was marshall of the parade. Then they had horse races on the Main Street track. Some men own some really beautiful horses. After the horse races, they had the foot races and I won in the ten to twelve year old race. I was the oldest one in that group because my birthday is in four days. My brothers teased me but I can use the prize money as well as anyone. There was a big tug-of-war and we Duclon boys made up half of one team. Too bad we lost. There was a tub race in the harbor and a pound boat race. Then we went down to the grove for the speeches. They are pretty dull, but everyone goes to listen anyway. Gustie Larson was there and she looked really grown up today. That's because her ma finally let her wear a dress that almost touched the ground. I'm sure glad I've grown past wearing knee pants and long black stockings. Gustie had her hair tied back with a bow and was wearing this dress with ruffles around the neck and she had on a gold locket. She looked real pretty. I wonder if she has a lock of some boy's hair in her locket already. I hope not. Most little boys were all dressed up in their sailor suits unless they were really little and then they wore sailor dresses. I can remember when Ma cut my hair and said I didn't have to wear dresses anymore. My brothers finally had to stop making fun of my sausage curls. There was a band playing in town most of the afternoon and a picnic was served to everyone who was there. Some little children had lemonade stands in front of their houses. Nick Kihl's Juddville String Band played for the evening dance and after dark, the town put on a big fireworks display. It was really something.

Jul. 7 -- I was in town today with Charlie and Oscar Anderson and we had a good laugh watching the summer people at the beach in their fancy swimming outfits. I don't know how they can stay afloat with all those clothes on. The ladies have these black wool suits with big sailor collars all trimmed in braid. They have wide black skirts with big woolen bloomers underneath and black stockings below that. Then they wear a white hat on top and swimming shoes on their feet. I guess they really don't swim much, just go wading. It's funny just to see ladies in short skirts with their legs sticking out below their skirts. I doubt we'll ever see Ma in one of those outfits. I hope she doesn't get mad when she reads this page in my journal about us laughing at the ladies' get-ups. Men can get by in just tight knee pants and high necked jerseys with sleeves to their elbows. When we go swimming down by our dock, we get by in a lot less than that.

Jul. 8 -- I am finally 13 years old. It sure feels a lot older than 12. Being Monday, everyone pretty much did their Monday work. Then Ambrose and Ada Belle and Wesley and Billy, and Will and Ruth and Julia all came out for supper to help me celebrate. Ma fixed a big pickerel with bread stuffing and tomato catsup and bacon on top and we had peas from the garden and cole slaw and potatoes and a huge platter of strawberry shortcake. I always ask for strawberry shortcake for my birthday supper unless we've had a real early spring and the strawberries are done for the year. It stays light so late that we were able to get in a good game of croquet after supper. Wes tried so hard to get up on our old stilts, but he never did make it up. Since we have such a large family, we don't give each other a lot of birthday presents but I got a brand new mouth organ from Ma and Pa with an instruction book and all. I hope I can get good at playing it. Anton Amundson lives in Ephraim and he's really good at it. Maybe he'll give me some pointers. Anton claims to be the second white child born in Ephraim. I wonder who the first one was.

Jul. 13 -- There are two grocery stores in town, Lundberg's on the corner, now owned by Mortons, and Hill's just north of Lundberg's. Hill's has a big room upstairs where they sometimes have dances. I finally got to go to a square dance there last night. Joe played the fiddle, Charlie played the stand-up bass, Edith Gehrke played the piano, and someone named Henry from Egg Harbor played the drums. I might have taken a turn with my guitar, but Gustie was there and I had a lot more fun dancing with her as my partner. She said I was a good dancer and I think she kind of likes me. She's going to the minstrel show at the Gibraltar town hall next Friday. Maybe I can meet her there. Once you are old enough, there are a lot of fun things to do around here, like husking bees in the evening by lantern light and house warmings and candy pulls. My oldest brothers like to play pool but I won't be old enough for quite a few years because minors aren't allowed in the pool halls. Two years ago, the town passed a lot of laws about pool halls and made the owners buy a license each year for $25. Myron Stevens is the Health Officer and he's in charge of enforcing the laws. Ma wouldn't like me being in a pool hall even if there were no laws.

Jul. 14 -- We all went way down to Sturgeon Bay today and back with Alfred Sorenson in his big boat. It was a good ride but pretty long. Yesterday's Advocate said that Engineer Ed Kenyon of the A.and W.is still having no end of trouble with folks living near the railroad track between Sturgeon Bay and Forestville. They have placed all sorts of obstacles on the tracks - logs, rocks, iron bolts etc. just to see what the effect will be on the locomotive. Kenyon says there have been no mishaps yet but the practice is dangerous.

Jul. 16 -- I went with some of the other boys to visit the Menominee campers down by the water in Fish Creek. Every summer, a big group of them comes over from Michigan on a Goodrich steamer. Some camp here for just a week or two, but some are here for the whole summer. The same ones come back every summer and we have a lot of fun with them.

Jul. 18 -- I picked cherries at Mr. Thorp's orchard today. He's glad to pay us boys to get the crop in. There was a gang of us so it didn't take long. I got to take a pail of cherries home to Ma who right away made two pies for supper tonight. She will can the rest tomorrow. The hardest work about cherries is pitting them, but Ma has this pitter that cranks and pokes out the pits, one at a time. Ma says she would rather use a hairpin herself. Either way, one of us always seems to get a pit in his piece of pie.

Jul. 20 -- Yesterday, I spent most of the day trimming the trees near the top of the bluff in front of the lighthouse and cutting away underbrush. We have to make sure our lighthouse can be seen from the water during the day too. All the bluffs along the shore here look a lot alike and even with charts, it can be hard for a boat captain to tell where he is. The early settlers named this township Gibraltar because the bluffs along the bay reminded them of the Rock of Gibraltar in Europe. Some light towers back east are even painted with black and white stripes and such so they can be seen more easily during the day. I read about the Statue of Liberty which is a really special looking lighthouse shaped like a lady holding a torch. It is in New York Harbor. It has an electric light inside of it. I've never seen an electric light but I don't think the lightkeeper would have to haul any fuel oil up the tower or trim any wicks or even wash any soot off the lens with an electric light. Maybe a lighthouse with an electric light in it doesn't even need a lightkeeper to live in it. That's something to think about. I went to the minstrel show in town last night with Jim and Joe but I sat with Gustie and her folks. It was funny to see grown men all made up to look like they were black men. The songs and jokes and skits were funny too.

Jul. 21 -- Mrs. Lundberg organized a Baptist Sunday School and I drove Ma in to one of their meetings this morning. They meet in the town hall now, but they are hoping to build a Baptist church in town before too long. That would please Ma. The Seventh Day Adventists built a church a few years ago on some land Asa Thorp gave them. When I was writing about the stores in town a few days back, I forgot to tell about the store Captain Ezra Graham and his wife operate out of their boat. They go back and forth between the towns during the season and stay three or four days in each place. There are shelves all around the inside of the hull. They pick up clothes from Lauerman Brothers in Marinette and hardware from Morley Murphy's in Green Bay. In fall, they haul the boat out and spend the winter in Fish Creek.

Jul. 23 -- Roy Thorp drove out to see Pa today in his buckboard. The Thorps are probably the most important people in Fish Creek. Increase Claflin was the first white man to settle in this area with his wife Mary Ann more than fifty years ago, but it was Asa Thorp who arrived from New York and built the main dock in town so he could sell wood to

BUCKBOARD

steamers operating on the bay. Then Asa's brother, Jacob, moved here too and he married Increase's daughter Maria, and Roy is their son. Roy has served as postmaster and town chairman and on the school board. His business is mostly fishing and farming. Asa's other brother, Levi, is the one who settled Egg Harbor real early on. Asa is pretty old now, in his seventies, I guess, but he sure keeps busy. He built the Thorp Hotel some years back as a boarding house for teachers and drummers who were in the area to sell their wares. Now he and his son Ted have moved a bunch of log houses, including Asa's first log cabin, in near to the hotel for cottages for all the city folks who want to spend the summer up here. Asa got into growing fruit awhile back and two years ago his peaches won a blue ribbon at the Chicago Exhibition. Some of the other important families in Fish Creek are the Kinseys who have about ten children and a lot of grandchildren and the Nobles who live at the main corner. Alex Noble is a blacksmith and he platted the town eastward. There's a couple of Hill families in town too. Old L.P. had been a lightkeeper on Beaver Island just like Pa. His sons own steamers and his one son Onnie is also good at pulling teeth.

Jul. 26 -- There must be about thirty families living on our point of land that sticks out into Green Bay between Fish Creek and Ephraim. It will be good to have our own school nearby come September. After chores today, I went over to Olsons and then a few of us boys climbed way up to

Sven Anderson's place on the highest bluff. He must have a pretty hard time climbing up his path in the winter but he sure has a good view. He never got married and he really likes to have us boys visit him. He always gives us something to eat before we leave. Ole Klungeland's place isn't too far from Sven's. He named it Blaasenberg which means windy mountain in Swedish. Now everyone calls the whole area around him Blossomberg and the new school that's going up will be called Blossomberg School. We didn't call on Ole. He lives in a real messy house and he hardly ever smiles and probably wouldn't even want visitors.

Jul. 28 -- The Roesers, who operate a lumber mill in Sister Bay, came over today in one of their biggest boats to have a picnic supper with us. I always have fun with their boys, especially Adolph, who is about my age.

Jul. 29 -- There was a lot of excitement around here today. We won't have to carry drinking water up from the bay any more because the Service is having a well dug. Ed Schreiber showed up first thing this morning with his well drilling outfit. He had to bring a treadmill that operates on horsepower in order to drill down through the rock ledge. The horse has to keep walking up a little slant on the treadmill in order not to slip backwards, and as it walks, the treadmill goes around and around and turns a belt that turns the drill. It's going to make life a lot easier for us to have drinking water right up here on the bluff near to the house, especially in the winter. There's a regular hand pump in the well like the one in the cistern. We'll keep using the soft water in the cistern for everything except drinking.

July 30 -- Mr. Schreiber had to drill down 70 feet before he found water but the pump is working and the water tastes real good.

Aug. 3 -- Ma has certain chores she wants done every Saturday. Maybe if there were some girls in our family we boys, especially the youngest ones, wouldn't have so many Saturday chores to do. In the winter we only use the kitchen in the house and in the summer we mostly just use the summer kitchen, but there's always some sweeping up and so on to do in the house kitchen. In the spring and fall, of course, there are two kitchens to clean. Now we're getting ready for another inspection so there's no cutting corners anyplace. The wood stoves get polished, dry sinks get scoured, and throw rugs get a good beating. On Saturdays, we take all the lamps and lanterns apart and trim the wicks and clean the chimneys and refill them with oil. The dining room chair seats all get scrubbed. Ma washes any windows that need it because she says we boys don't use enough elbow grease to shine them good. She always scrubs the kitchen floor in the house last of all and then puts down newspapers to keep it clean until it dries. The worst Saturday job is scrubbing up the privy. Our privy has two holes for grownups and one smaller lower down hole for little children. We also have to sweep down the spider webs in the privy. We only use our chamber pot and commode on the coldest winter nights. I feel sorry for the girls who clean guest cottages and hotel rooms and have to empty all those chamber pots every morning all summer. Every room in a hotel has its own bowl and pitcher and slop jar to clean daily too. We mostly do our washing up in the kitchens. In the summer we have all that grass to mow too whether it needs it or not. Seems like the only day anyone gets a chance to use the hammock is Sunday.

Aug. 5 -- The steamer Arcadia arrived today with a load of Cream City bricks from Milwaukee just like the ones used to build the lighthouse. The government finally got around to allotting the money to build us a separate oil house off aways from the lighthouse. It will be able to hold 90 five gallon cans of kerosene. Up until now, we've been storing the oil in the separate cellar under the light tower. When we were still using lard oil for the lamp that was all right, but since the lamp was switched over to burn kerosene a few years back, it was really dangerous to store kerosene oil right under the tower. Kerosene catches fire more easily than lard oil and if lightning were to strike the tower, our whole place could go up in flames. We've been storing the empty oil cans in a little room upstairs we call the tin room. Now we'll be able to store the empty cans in the new oil house too until the tender brings a new supply of oil and takes the empty tins away to be used again. Ma already has plans to fix up the tin room for a sewing room and a guest room for when people stay over.

That's good news for us boys because we won't have Service people sharing our room and snoring all night. George Sylvester from the Service came to build the new oil house and he will be living with us until the supply boat arrives. He plans to have the oil house finished by then and he's going to put up a flag pole and make some repairs as well.

THE OIL HOUSE

Aug. 8 -- We were talking tonight about the storm we had three years ago today. It was so bad that it blew the top right off parts of the stone wall in front of the lighthouse. Being high on a bluff, at least we never have to worry about waves washing over the lighthouse like they've had happen at Cana Island. The Cana light tower is the tallest brick building in Door County. That lighthouse was setting on such low ground that waves swept right through it during the Alpena storm. They had to haul enough gravel to fill in a half acre of land around the lighthouse to protect it from future storms.

Aug. 11 -- I helped with the grain harvesting over at Sorenson's today. We stood it in shocks to dry after it was cut. Next we'll thresh it with a flail to separate the kernels of grain from the heads of the stalks of straw. Some farmers south of here who have bigger fields, get together to help each other thresh with a big threshing machine. After supper, Ma and I picked raspberries in the garden and thimbleberries at the edge of the woods. The gooseberries are ripening too and I sure hate hulling them. We're starting to get a lot of vegetables from the garden now. It's a lot of work to put it all up but it sure tastes good in the middle of winter.

Aug. 12 -- Ma's got her heart set on getting the tin room all fixed up before inspection. We scrubbed it all good today and tomorrow we'll paint. Ma plans to move her treadle sewing machine in there and maybe her spinning wheel too, if there's room after a bed gets in there.

Aug. 16 -- We sure have been hustling to get ready for inspection. We have wooden walks leading to all the outbuildings except the new oil house and some of the planks needed replacing so we helped George Sylvester get the job done today. What with our new supplies arriving any day now, we have to have the cellar all cleaned and ready too. The Advocate said it was just a year ago that the largest gathering of people Sturgeon Bay has ever seen turned out to celebrate the completion of the Ahnapee and Western Railroad to the city. Of the crowd estimated at 4000, about half came from outside the city by invitation. Eleven coaches arrived from Green Bay and about 350 people arrived by flatcar from Ahnapee. Hundreds more came in on the Hart excursion boats. There were speeches by important people and Louis P. Nebel arranged a special salute. He drilled about 30 holes in solid rock down by his quarry and filled them with powder. Then at noon when the cannon located at the bridge approach went off to announce the arrival of the train from Ahnapee, he set off the blasts one after the other. I wish I could have been there. Sturgeon Bay will probably never have a day such as that again.

Aug. 17 -- All the men, including us older boys, worked to finish up the new schoolhouse. It was almost like a barn raising. It just shows what you can get done in a short time when a lot of people work together on something. The ladies brought over a picnic lunch at noon so the day seemed more like a holiday than a working day. The school is made out of logs. Mr. Gustaphson is in charge of building it.

Aug. 19 -- Beans were ready for canning today so I helped Ma wash and string them and cut them up. Then she cooked them in a big kettle. While they were cooking, she washed the mason jars and zinc lids and scalded them with boiling water. Then she put the hot beans and some salt brine in the jars and put a rubber ring around the neck of each jar. A zinc lid goes on top of the rubber ring and gets screwed down real tight. Then she put the jars of beans in a big kettle of water that has to boil for more than a half hour. All that cooking kills any germs in the jars and when the jars are taken out of the water bath as Ma calls it, and they cool down, the lid seals down real good and keeps germs from getting in and spoiling the food. People have been known to die from eating food that wasn't canned real carefully. Ma will be busy with preserving food for winter for the next month or more.

Aug. 21 -- Ma and I went out collecting mushrooms today. You can't eat just any kind of mushrooms because some are poisonous. We got out the special rack Pa made for drying the mushrooms in the sun. Ma keeps turning over the mushrooms and putting them lower on the rack until they're real dry, all the time adding newly picked mushrooms at the top of the rack. There's a lot of water in mushrooms, but when they are finally dried out, you can keep them for months to use in soup and stew and such. We picked a big bouquet of goldenrod too. Dried goldenrod looks kind of pretty but Ma always keeps it outside because it makes some people sneeze.

Aug. 23 -- Ma finished up her latest crazy quilt just in time to enter it in the county fair. Her good friend, Rachel Norton, took it along to Sturgeon Bay for the judging today. If Ma doesn't win a blue ribbon, it will be the first time. This quilt will go to the bride of the next brother to get married. Ada Belle and Ruth already have their quilts. Frank's more than old enough to get married but he's not courting anyone that I know of. He's been talking about putting up a house of his own on some of the Shanty Bay property he bought. Joe's been over to Baileys Harbor to see Augusta Spring a lot lately so maybe he'll be the next one to get married.

Aug. 27 -- Aunt Rachel brought Ma's quilt back from the fair and sure enough it had a blue ribbon on it. One of these years I'll be old enough to take myself to the fair. By then, I suppose I'll be too busy doing other things to go all the way to Sturgeon Bay to a fair. A lot of folks go and stay over, but Pa always has the light to tend, of course.

Aug. 28 -- The supply boat arrived today so we had a busy day unloading everything and getting it stowed away. Some months back, Ma and Pa had to fill out a requisition, it's called. On it, they listed all the supplies they would need to operate the light for the next year and to maintain the property. Besides the fuel for the lamp, Pa orders lamp parts, polish, sponges, paint, sandpaper, whatever forms he needs for his reports, pencils, paint brushes, brooms, soap and so on. Pa gets a salary of $50 a month but on top of that, he can order food that will keep real good like salt pork, corned beef, summer sausage, potatoes, apples, rice, beans, vinegar, coffee, popcorn and of course, big barrels of flour and sugar and corn meal and such. Ma needs a lot of those things to keep this big family fed. Just to have enough bread on hand she has to bake six loaves of bread a couple of times a week. The supplies for the lamp had to be carried down into the separate cellar under the tower or up to the closet off the upstairs hall. The food all had to be carried down to the cellar under the house and stored just so. Ma's real particular about her cellar and has all her home canning lined up real orderly on the shelves. She's been busy putting up pickles and kraut too so those crocks are in one corner. We go into Fish Creek to the store real often, but it's nice to know we have that whole cellar full of food in case the weather is such that we can't go into town. Our lighthouse cost $12,000 to build and I think it was so expensive because they had to blast away a lot of limestone to make the cellar.

Aug. 31 -- It's the last day of August so that means summer's about over. Ma and Pa had a big party here tonight and some of the folks, like the Ephraim Andersons and the Sister Bay Lundbergs, are staying overnight. McCummingses and Sorensons and Weborgs don't have so far to go. Word had it that John Anclam bought the dock, grocery store and post office in Baileys Harbor from Frederick Wohltman. With the weather being so hot lately, folks from this side of the county have been spending more time over on the Lake Michigan side to keep cool. That's the excuse Joe uses to go over to Baileys Harbor so often but we know it's more than the weather that he's going over for.

Sept. 1 -- Except for Jim and me, all the brothers and the two wives got to go to a real wingding of a wedding last night in Baileys Harbor. It was a double wedding because Augusta Appel married August Jackson, and her sister, Ella Appel, married John Leidel. There were two ministers too. I helped Ma watch over the three grandchildren at our place. A dance at Jorn's Hall followed the ceremony and our people didn't get home until almost dawn.

Sept. 3 -- Yesterday was Labor Day and that means the end of the summer visitors. All the city school children had to be back in school today. The Menominee campers are all gone too. It seems every summer there are more people here for a vacation. A good vacation for me would be a trip to Green Bay or to someplace real far away like Milwaukee or Chicago or St. Louis. It would be even more fun to go someplace far away on a train or on one of the big steamers of the Goodrich Line.

Sept. 6 -- Ma has been canning up a storm for the last few weeks. Seems like everything comes ripe at the same time. She has done up a lot of tomatoes and has jars of catsup and chili sauce too and even tomato jam. Any tomatoes that aren't ripe enough to eat before the first frost will be put up in green tomato mincemeat for pie. To make that, Ma uses tomatoes, chopped apples, lemon rind, brown sugar, raisins, currants and spices. She cooks it all up together and puts it in jars. When she makes a pie of it, she just puts a little butter on before the top crust and she doesn't even have to put any meat in it. It doesn't sound all that good but it sure tastes good. Then there's the late season pickles like crab apples and slippery Jims. Slippery Jims are made out of the big overripe cucumbers. Ma cans some peaches for sauce, some she pickles and some she makes into jam. I picked wild grapes for jelly that she drips through some cheesecloth so it's nice and clear. She makes quince and gooseberry jelly that way too. The early apples are ready now too and they aren't good keepers so she puts some up as sauce. When the fruits and vegetables are done, she will begin canning any game that we get and can't eat up right away. Wild ducks and geese will be coming through soon and there's always grouse and pheasants and such. Ma works mighty hard to keep us eating good so I don't mind helping her out a little.

Sept. 9 -- I spent my first day in the new Blossomberg School. I have less than two miles to go to school. Our teacher, Miss Higgins said we should feel kind of special being the first class to attend a brand new school. I helped a little to build it but I didn't see it all finished until today. The teacher's desk is up front and has a big slate on the wall behind it for her to write on. On the side walls are pictures of our most beloved presidents, according to Miss Higgins, George Washington and Abraham Lincoln, and a picture of President Cleveland is over the slate. In the front corner of the room is a tall stool and if someone misbehaves, he has to sit on the stool and wear this silly pointed hat that says DUNCE on it. Then right in front of the teacher's desk are the recitation benches. She calls us up in groups to do our lessons with her. Sometimes we take turns reading out loud and other times we do our arithmetic problems on our slates. When we're not up front reciting, we're expected to tend to our assignments and we older ones are to help the younger ones when they need it. There's a stove almost in the middle of the room and it will be the job of us older boys to keep wood alongside of it when the weather turns cold. There's a place to hang our coats and keep our lunch pails right by the door. That's where the water pail and dipper are too, but we can't get a drink without permission. In the middle of the morning and again in the middle of the afternoon, we get to have recess. We can play baseball or marbles or mumblety-peg. That's a game you play with pocket knives in the dirt. The girls mostly play jacks or roll hoops or just sit around making flower chains. We're supposed to use the privy during recess too so we don't have to ask to use it during class. If we can't play outside because of the weather, Miss Higgins said we could have recess inside and play checkers or Parcheesi or Around the World with Nellie Bly or hide the button. Jim started school today too, but he's thinking of quitting when the fall fishing picks up. Funny thing, we boys just wear our every day clothes to school, but most of the girls had these starched white apron things on over their everyday dresses. They call them pinafores, I guess. Miss Higgins said I had real nice handwriting for a boy. Maybe that's because of all the practice I've been getting writing in this journal. She seemed a little surprised to hear about all the books I've read from the lighthouse traveling library. I think I'm going to like going to a regular school. So far, the only thing I didn't like about it was sitting next to John Anderson at lunchtime while he ate his molasses and raw onion sandwiches.

Sept. 11 -- In school today, we were talking about what Door County was like before white men settled here. Miss Higgins thinks that Jean Nicolet probably stopped at Horseshoe Island on his way to Red Banks. He was a French fur trader. Father Alouez and Father Andre might have stopped in this area to try to convert the Indians to Christianity. The Indians were mostly from the Potowatomi and Winnebago tribes but some, like the Ottawa-Hurons, were driven here from the east by the warlike Iroquois. Miss Higgins said there was a big Indian village where Heins Creek empties into Lake Michigan near Jacksonport and that a big battle with the Iroquois took place there. A lot of Indians used to live right near our lighthouse at Shanty Bay. Miss Higgins said we should keep our eyes open for flint arrowheads and marked stones and such. Most of the Indians moved out of these parts after their land was turned over to the government about 60

GREEN BAY

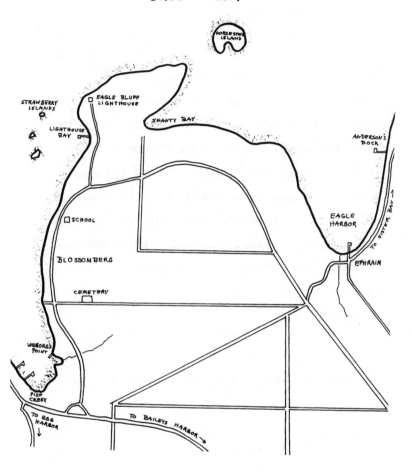

LIGHTHOUSE POINT

89

years ago. The few who stayed around keep pretty much to themselves.

Sept. 14 -- Being Saturday, I didn't have to go to school so I went over to Sorensons' to get in the last cutting of hay. It's hard to believe that every farm field around here was once a forest and someone had to pull out all the stumps of cut trees before it could be plowed and planted. On the way home, I saw some dolls eyes and I picked some for Ma to dry. They are wildflowers with red stems and white berries that have black dots in the middle, just like dolls eyes. She was happy to get them.

Sept. 17 -- The orchards are at their peak right now so after school Jim and I went picking. Besides apples, we got some plums and pears for Ma to can. She'll make some plum kuchen with the fresh plums first though. Pa says fruit trees do real well in these parts because the big bodies of water, Lake Michigan and Green Bay, make a spring frost less likely. When the trees are in blossom is when you have to worry about a frost. I guess the cool damp climate makes for slow hardy growth as well. I suppose some other lightkeepers are harvesting hops now. It's pretty common for keepers to plant hops for making beer. Being a Baptist, Ma doesn't allow any beer making in her house.

Sept. 20 -- School is going good. I'm one of the oldest ones there but I don't mind helping the younger ones. Miss Higgins is real nice so I like helping her with the chores as well. Geography is my favorite subject and arithmetic is my least favorite subject. In the mail today was another citation for Pa for having the best looking lighthouse at the August inspection. He says we all deserve credit for it. With all the other lighthouses in the county, it really is a matter of family pride to get a citation. I wonder if the Browns know we got it.

Sept. 22 -- We got our first light frost last night. It only nipped Ma's flowers a little. It probably did more damage to gardens that aren't as high up as ours and aren't as close to the water. Being we didn't have school today, Jim and I spent all day making wood. There was some downed wood near to the lighthouse property that we could take, and there was a dead tree at the top of the bluff that Frank had already cut down for us to saw up. We also collected all the driftwood that had washed ashore. We hitched Queenie to the wagon for bringing the wood back to the house. We needed to use the two-man saw on the bigger tree trunks but we could just use the buck saw on the smaller ones. After sawing the wood into chunks, we took turns splitting it with a wedge and a mall. Pa always says with wood you make heat twice, once when you're sweating to cut and split it, and again when you burn it. I don't even remember what it looked like in these parts before most of the big trees were cut down for steamer fuel and for lumber. Probably everyone thought it would be impossible to ever run out of big trees but already they are getting scarce. We piled some of the wood in the lean-to next to the kitchen because we're beginning to light the stove in the house more and more these cool mornings. When the stove is going all day, that means we have hot water in its reservoir for cleaning up and for washing the dishes and such. Because the cook stove in the kitchen is down four steps from the rest of the house, that's the only stove we need to burn now because the heat from it rises and heats the rest of the house when it's not yet real cold outside. Last night, Jim and Charlie taught me how to play a card game called sheepshead. I guess they finally decided I was old enough to play it with them. Anyway, Joe's spending more and more time with Gustie Spring these days and it takes three to play.

Sept. 27 -- Seems like Ma just finished spring housecleaning and she's already starting her fall housecleaning. She asked me if I'd strain up her cord bedstead for her tomorrow. There's holes drilled in the side and end bars of the bed and then hemp rope is strung from side to side and then from end to end through the holes. After awhile, the rope stretches and that allows the bed to sag so you can't sleep tight. Sometimes it's enough to just put a stick in and twist it to take up the slack, but this time, Ma says it needs redoing. For straining it up, you need a wooden wrench with an iron handle to strain the cord tight at each hole and then you drive a pointed wooden plug into the hole with a mallet to hold the cord tight while you release the wrench and go around to the next hole opposite to pull up the slack. It's a little like caning a chair the way you put in plugs to hold your last piece of cane in place until you weave your way over to the next hole. Ma is going to make a new mattress for their bed too. I'm not sure if this one will be of husk or straw. A mattress made out of corn husks is harder for sleeping on, but it lasts a lot longer than one made of oat straw because straw breaks up sooner than husks. Ma made a new feather tick to go on top of the mattress from the down I helped strip last winter.

Sept. 29 -- Yesterday and last night we had a really bad storm. It was a gale from the north and it went on for twenty hours. We had all the shutters secured the whole time which meant it was pitch black in the house, even during the day. Pa didn't want to take a chance that they would blow off again. No damage was done to the lighthouse, but there were lots of tree limbs down in the area so I spent part of today gathering up kindling and sawing up bigger branches. When the wind is off shore as it was yesterday, we sure get the brunt of it, perched out here on the bluff as we are. The eagles that can still find a tall tree to nest in around here don't seem to be bothered one bit by a big wind.

SHUTTERED FOR THE STORM

Sept. 30 -- This month went real fast with regular school starting. Today Ma was cleaning the dining room, wiping down the wainscoting and all. I hope she doesn't decide it needs another coat of paint before winter. The dining room rug is made from an old piece of carpeting Ma cut up, so I took it out to the clothesline after school and beat it good for her. Tomorrow, Ma wants us to help get the storm windows up. The leaves are starting to change color and I heard geese flying over today. Pa has to spend more and more time tending the lamp as the nights get longer.

Oct. 5 -- Being Saturday, I spent most of the day helping Sorensons cut and shock their corn. When it's dry, we'll pull the cobs off the stalks and then pull the husks off the ears of corn. Stored in a crib with spaces between the slats, corn will keep a whole year. There was a big story in today's Advocate about last week's storm. It really was the worst one in a long time. Another story was about a Dr. Kloss who is going to build a sanitarium in Fish Creek. I'm not sure if that's the same as a hospital or not, but the paper said one was long needed in these parts.

Oct. 9 -- After school today, I got to use the apple press to make cider. The press squeezes a pailful of apples at a time and the juice drips out of the bottom between slats. Then the juice has to be strained and put in scalded jugs. We get to drink as much of it as we want before it turns to vinegar. The older boys always want to try making some apple jack but Ma always says no. I think apple jack is like a wine you get when you add sugar to cider and let it ferment.

Oct. 12 -- Frank turned 24 today and some folks from town, Barringers, Churches and Nobles, came out to the light to help him celebrate. The boys got out their instruments and this time I played right along. Not only am I getting pretty good on the guitar now, but I could play my mouth organ instead on some of the numbers. Frank had his violin out of course, the one he says is a Stradivarius or whatever the name is. He got it from a sailor who wanted some cash in the worst way. I wonder what is so great about a Stradivarius anyway. I guess it's just named after the man who made it.

Oct. 16 -- Fishing is back in full swing now so my older brothers are kept pretty busy. A lot of fishermen do pound net fishing. They hang a big kettle shaped net on stakes driven into the bottom of the bay. It has a narrow tunnel of net leading into it and two wing nets which lead the fish into the tunnel. Once the fish are trapped in it, they can't find their way out through the narrow tunnel. Then the men come alongside in boats and loosen the ropes holding the net to the stakes and pull up the net into a tight bag. Then they use dip nets to scoop the wriggling fish into their open boats. My brothers brought some of their catch home yesterday to smoke. First they soak the fish in a salt brine for a few hours. Then they hang them up in the smokehouse on sticks to drip for awhile. Then they build a fire out of maple wood for the smoking. Smoked fish will keep for a pretty long time but they sure do taste best when they are freshly smoked. We had some for supper tonight. This is a real pretty time of the year. The trees have all turned to red and yellow and orange, except the pine trees of course and they look real dark green this time of year. The air is so clear that almost every day we can see the Michigan shore across the bay.

Oct. 19 -- We got word that Capt. Stanley died on the 13th. He was the keeper at Eagle Bluff from when it was built until Pa took over. According to his log, there must have been visitors to the light almost every day. The Stanleys sure had a lot of company and a lot of parties that lasted until the next morning. Of course you can't blame people for not wanting to return to Fish Creek or Ephraim through the woods or over the water or ice after dark. Capt. Stanley was transferred to the Sherwood light near Sturgeon Bay after 15 years here. His daughter had just died unexpectedly and his wife wanted to be closer to their doctor who was also their son-in-law. Their son died while they were living here too. I was too little to remember them but Pa says they were real nice folks. Kinseys moved into Fish Creek last week so I went into town today to see where they live. Then a bunch of us boys went over to Schuyler's smithy to watch George work. While we were there, Levi Vorous brought his horse in to be shod so we stayed around to watch that. First George trims the horse's hooves. Then he picks out a shoe that's about the right size. He heats the horseshoe on his forge until the shoe is white hot. Then he shapes it on an anvil with his hammer and then plunges it into water to cool. He tries it on the horse and if it fits real good, he nails it on the horse's hoof. If not, he heats it up again for more shaping. Seems it would hurt the horse to have nails driven into its hooves but I guess it doesn't.

Oct. 20 -- Today wasn't very exciting but we did get in a winter's supply of hazelnuts. We have to go some ways into the woods to get them but once there, the heavy clusters of nuts are pretty easy to pick. We always take along a hoe to pull down the higher branches. Ma's never satisfied until we have several big sacks full of nuts.

Oct. 21 -- Miss Higgins was telling us about the geography of our county today. She said scientists think this part of Wisconsin was once covered with a glacier. That's a blanket of ice that moved down over the land from the north when the climate got colder. The moving ice gouged out the harbors on the bay side of the county and carried a lot of rocks with it as it pushed its way south. The slowly moving ice couldn't budge the limestone cliffs though. Then as the climate warmed, the glacier gradually melted and got smaller and smaller starting from the south edge. As it melted, it left behind all the rocks that cover the county and have to be picked out of the farm fields every spring. Miss Higgins said there might have been more than one glacier that moved south over the land and then melted back north again. It's pretty hard to imagine, but then if it really did happen, I guess it was a long time ago. I sure like our new well. One of my chores is to see that the two water pails on the dry sink are filled each morning before school. The galvanized pail holds rain water from the cistern for washing up and so on, and the white enamel pail with the dipper in it holds water from the new well for drinking and cooking. I have to pump up and down awhile to get the water up out of the well but that's still a lot easier than carrying it

STEPS TO THE DOCK

up the steep steps from the bay. I'll always remember one time when Professor Moss came over from Ephraim in his boat with his daughter Mary and son Charlie. Those Moss children were taught to mind their father without asking questions. It's a good thing they did because that day, Mary was going down our steps to the dock and Charlie was behind her and Dr. Moss was last. Charlie slipped and started falling down the steps and Dr. Moss yelled to Mary to sit down. She obeyed right away and kept Charlie from falling all the way down the steps and taking her with him.

Oct. 23 -- Every day for the last week I have caught a mouse in both the traps I keep set. One trap is in the summer kitchen and the other is in the house kitchen. The mice are looking for a warm place to spend the winter, I guess, because every October it's the same. I usually just take the traps outside and let the mice go because I don't like killing them. Joe makes fun of me and says I'm probably catching the same mice over and over again.

Oct. 25 -- Ma always keeps vegetable scraps like potato peels and such in a pot on the stove to cook a little before I take them out to the pigs. I was thinking today when I was carrying out the scraps that it will soon be time for butchering. I never have liked butchering day. Pa heard that Capt. Graham is going to have a store in his warehouse on the dock this winter. He'll be selling the goods left from his barge store. Some say he's thinking of building a house in Fish Creek. The barge store business must have been good this past season.

Oct. 26 -- We're about done with the garden for another year. The squash and pumpkins are all down cellar and the cabbage is either stored or made into kraut. Ma has a board with knife-sharp cutters in it that we use to shred a half a head of cabbage at a time. We've been raking up leaves and carrying them over to the garden. Tomorrow I'll maybe start spading them under to rot and make the soil better.

Oct. 28 -- There was pretty much Fish Creek news in Saturday's Advocate. The Anderson boys made a record lift of 1500 pounds of fish last week that sold for $80. That's four $20 gold pieces for one week of fishing. Fish Creek is now the largest fishing station on Green Bay. Then there was mention of the Salvation Army meetings being held in the town hall and a little article about the new schoolhouse just being completed in town. Seems like this is the year for new schoolhouses. Asa Thorp sold some of his land along the water to Dr. Welker for his resort. The doctor is even thinking about moving a big building across the ice from Michigan to use as a hotel and casino. That would sure be interesting to see. There was a letter to the editor about President Cleveland saying he's the first president to become a millionaire while in office. Seems there's a lot of people who don't think much of him as a president.

Nov. 1 -- Last night was Halloween and as usual there were some goings on in Fish Creek. I'm not going to put down any names because I don't want to get anyone in this family in trouble, but a group of boys rigged a wire to the bell in the Episcopal church and lo and behold, it began to ring like crazy at about ten o'clock at night. Some of the men from the neighborhood went running over there in their night clothes with coats over, but by the time they got there and figured out what was going on, the bell ringers were long gone. Ma didn't allow me to be in town that late on a school night, but I got the story from the horse's mouth, you might say.

Nov. 3 -- The tender Dahlia was out on Frying Pan Reef yesterday taking the buoys off for the season. It will be stopping by here soon for our final inspection of the year. It's been getting real cold nights and Pa thinks the bay might freeze over early this year. This time of year, Pa has to tend the light for almost 14 hours.

Nov. 9 -- I like writing in this journal more when something really exciting happens, like today. A steam barge out of Port Huron ran aground on Jack Island and we had to put out in the rescue boat to get the crew off in case the barge broke up. Lucky for me, it happened on a Saturday so I was at home instead of in school. Jim and Joe were off hunting and only Charlie and Frank were home so they asked me to come along. When it was all over they both said I was a real big help. It doesn't look very far out to Jack Island over the water, but it seemed to take forever to get there. It was blowing pretty good too, so it was a wild ride. The captain and two of his men decided to stay with the barge and we brought the rest of the crew back to the lighthouse to stay the night. One of the crew is only

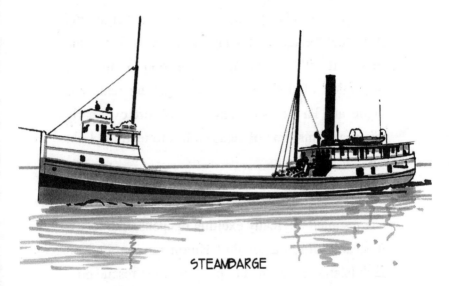

STEAMBARGE

a few years older than I am and he seemed pretty scared. November storms can be real bad. It was three or four years ago this month when Horace Larson and Charlie Jones capsized off the southeast point of Chambers Island. Horace drowned but Charlie swam ashore and was saved.

Nov. 10 -- When the wind went down today, the steam barge was able to back off the shoal with the help of two boats from town. We put the crewmen back on the barge and it was underway again. Miss Higgins wants me to write a story about what it's like to live in a lighthouse. I can use this journal for ideas. It would be a lot different to live in a really isolated lighthouse, like on an island. You might not see other people or get into a town for weeks on end. I remember reading about a girl named Abbie who was about my age and lived in a lighthouse off the coast of Maine. Her Pa was away from the island getting supplies and her Ma was sick and a big storm came up and her Pa couldn't get back and she had to tend two lamps all by herself for four weeks. That must have been a real scary time for her.

Nov. 12 -- I came down with a really bad cough and sore throat today. Ma says maybe I got chilled on Saturday helping to rescue those crewmen. She said I should stay home from school so she could fix me up. First she boiled up some Stewed Quaker for me to eat. That's an awful mess of molasses, onions and vinegar. Then she made a poultice of warm milk and bread that she put on my throat and wrapped a flannel rag on top of the poultice. One ear was bothering me a little so she made me keep a warm onion heart in my ear. I drank herb tea all day and I guess I really do feel better.

Nov. 13 -- The inspector showed up today and brought some Service workers to overhaul the lamp while he made his inspection. We don't worry quite so much about the fall inspection as the summer one. Maybe that's because the yard has been tended to until next spring, and the summer kitchen isn't being used much any more. Ma just finished her fall housecleaning too so the house is in good shape. Pa should have only a month or six weeks left to tend the light this season. I'll be going back to school tomorrow.

Nov. 16 -- I went down to Blossomberg with the Tenneson boys today and we stopped by at Peter Weborg's cooperage. This time of the year he's really working hard to make enough barrels for the fish salting season. The wooden staves have to fit together real tight top and bottom to make sure the salt brine from the fish won't leak out on the way to market. Some fish will be sent as far as the east coast. There's even railroad cars that can be kept cold for taking things like fish to the cities out east. You would think they could catch enough fish out there in the ocean without getting more from here. John Brown has a cooperage too near the harbor in town. Seems he's always putting together a jigsaw puzzle when he's not putting together a barrel.

Nov. 17 -- I finally shot my first game. I was out with Joe this afternoon using Jim's gun and I spotted a rabbit sitting real still, hoping I wouldn't see him. I took a shot and hit him squarely. I'm glad I didn't just wound him. That happened to Jim one time when I was out with him and it's pitiful to hear a wild thing crying out as it runs away wounded. Joe said I must have a pretty good eye. He showed me how to skin and clean the rabbit and cut it up. After it's soaked overnight in salt water, Ma will make a pie of it with carrots and onions inside a crust. Joe and I plan to go hunting again after school tomorrow. The coons start to come out about dusk.

Nov. 19 -- Butchering is over for another year. After Pa sticks the pigs in the neck with his knife and they bleed out, he hangs them upside down. Then he scalds them in boiling water and we all take a turn scraping the bristles off. When Pa gets the pigs all cut up, the hams and bacons get soaked in brine before being smoked in a smudge from green hickory sticks. We always make balloons out of the pigs' bladders by blowing air in them and then drying them by the stove. Ma is always in a hurry to get the sausage made out of the rest of the meat that isn't cut into chops and roasts and such. We have a meat grinder and a sausage stuffer that we bolt to the old table in the summer kitchen. Ma cleans the intestines real good for the sausage casings and she's in charge of adding the seasonings, but I do most of the grinding and stuffing. When the links of sausage are all ready, they will get smoked too. Then Ma still has to render all the fat into lard. She uses the cracklins that are left from rendering to make potato sausage. One of my favorite suppers is fried potato sausage and apple sauce.

Nov. 24 -- I got to go to the free Thanksgiving dance in Baileys Harbor last night. Ma said I could go with my brothers if I behaved myself and if they would come home at a reasonable hour. I haven't seen Gustie for a long time so I was real glad to see her there with her folks. I'm getting so I can dance most of the squares now. The Browns from the Cana light were there, of course, but we all stayed out of trouble. The McCummingses were all there too, De Witt, DeHart, DeLos, DeEtte and Adeline. They must have run out of DeSomething names when they got to Adeline. Their Pa, David McCummings built the second pier and sawmill in Fish Creek.

Nov. 25 -- Local fishermen including my brothers have been real busy hauling in nets full of herring with their Mackinaws. Mackinaws are double ended sailboats that are about thirty or forty feet long and are real lean and fast. If there isn't enough wind to sail they use a long sweep oar for sculling. Half the townsfolk of Fish Creek are down at the dock helping with the fish salting this week, even the women and children. I helped for awhile after school. It's almost like a corn husking party the way everyone pitches in and has a good time together. Sometimes even some drinking and jigging goes on. After the head and entrails are removed from the fish, the scales are scrubbed off with coarse salt. That's the part that's real hard on the hands. Then the fish are put in a wooden vat for washing. After they dry a little on the drying table, they are layered in barrels with salt between the layers. Boats from both the Hill and Hart lines are used to get the fish to the wholesale markets before the bay freezes over. Ma's been pickling herring to store in crocks along with everything else down cellar.

Nov. 29 -- Yesterday was Thanksgiving and we had a real good family gathering here. Ammie and Bill and their families were all here for a big dinner and then everyone stayed the night. Ma had been baking bread and cookies and pies and such all week. Ma always has at least two kinds of cookies stored in crocks, sugar cookies and molasses cookies, but she made some other kinds as well this week including my favorite sour cream cookies. Ma got out her best tablecloth, the red and white one that she's had since she and Pa were married, and used her good blue and white dishes and the table looked real special. We had duck, venison and pork roast, white potatoes and sweet potatoes, raisin stuffing, two kinds of beans, squash, turnips, and boiled onions, and for dessert, mince meat, apple and pumpkin pies and rice pudding. We men slept in the hay loft between layers of Ma's older patchwork quilts, and the mothers and children slept in the house. This morning, Ma was up early fixing corned beef hash with poached eggs on top and buckwheat pancakes with freshly smoked sausages. When I went to bed last night, I didn't think I could eat for a week, but I sure tied into the pancakes and hash this morning. It's fun having the grandchildren around. They like it when Pa lets them drink out of his mustache cup. Pa has his own supply of lemon drops that he keeps up on the shelf next to the clock and he makes them ask real polite before he gives them any candy. Pa asked Ammie's oldest boy if he would like an apple from the cellar but then he brought him up a potato instead. We all had a good laugh at the look on Wes' face when Pa handed him the potato. We got to remembering Thanksgiving Day six years ago when the steamer the City of Luddington went aground in Shanty Bay and Pa and all the older boys had to leave their dinner to help out. I was too little to help but I remember all the commotion.

Nov. 30 -- It's been so cold lately that all the boats from around here are in winter storage. That doesn't mean Pa can put out the light for the season yet, because there's still some big boats headed for the port of Green Bay for the winter, and some that want to get out into the big lake before the bay freezes over. I only have one more month to go on my journal assignment.

Dec. 7 -- The bay is frozen all the way across now so Pa can put out the light for the season and get everything stored away proper. Now that we don't use the cellar under the tower for storing fuel, he can store extra lamp chimneys and such down there. This is really early for the bay to freeze over. One winter, it never did freeze completely, but in February the Inspector ordered the light be put out anyway and not relit until April. Pa is happy to get an early start on his winter break.

Dec. 9 -- There's usually good fishing across the bay near the Michigan shore in December, but with the bay freezing over so early, the boys won't be moving their operation over there until the ice gets thick enough to use iceboats. Miss Higgins passed out parts for a Christmas program we are going to put on at school next week. She asked me to be the narrator because I'm one of the oldest and the best reader, she says. At least I get to read my part and don't have to memorize it like the others do. If Jim hadn't quit when fishing picked up he might have been the narrator instead of me.

Dec. 10 -- Saturday's Advocate said that Christmas trees from our area are being hauled to Chicago by train this year. There was also an article about the two new life saving stations that have just been completed, one at Plum Island and one at Baileys Harbor. It was a good thing that our lighthouse was equipped as a life saving station and that my brothers were trained to make rescues when that barge went aground a few weeks ago. The first lighthouse in this area was built on Rock Island off Washington Island about 30 years ago. It's hard to believe that little Rock Island was once the largest settlement in Door County. The Plum Island and Pilot Island lighthouses in Death's Door came next. With 250 miles of shoreline in Door County you can see why there are more lighthouses here than any other county in the United States. Besides the Cana Island lighthouse north of Baileys Harbor, there's the range lights right in the village. One range light is in the window of a lighthouse 300 yards inland, and the other range light is in a little building on the shore. When a boat is heading into the harbor, the captain just has to keep the two lights lined up one above the other to make a safe landing.

Dec. 13 -- I feel sorry for the little children who are worried about Santa Claus having enough snow to make the trip on Christmas Eve. We got a real nice snowfall Tuesday night but on Wednesday the snow changed to rain and all the snow washed away. When the temperature dropped below freezing again on Thursday, the ice on the bay froze real smooth. It is so smooth that the town boys have been playing baseball on skates in the harbor the last couple of days. I'm hoping to get in on the fun tomorrow if Ma doesn't have too many extra chores lined up around here for me to do. The folks went across the ice into town tonight in the cutter to hear Dr. Kloss, from the new sanitarium, lecture on Good Health and How To Preserve It. I think Ma probably knows as much about preserving good health as he does.

Dec. 15 -- There's a new lightkeeper on Chambers Island. His name is Capt. Christianson.

We'll be going to visit there when the ice is thick. It's about three miles across and then a mile or so around to the north side of the island. The government built the lighthouse there right after they built ours and they used pretty much the same plan. The first keeper was Lewis Williams and he had eleven children living in a house the same size as ours. I guess we can't complain about being crowded. Chambers Island is real nice and even has a lake on it. There aren't many other inland lakes in Door County.

Dec. 16 -- We boys were talking together about a Christmas present for Ma. I have a little money saved from picking cherries so I can be in on it too this year. There was an advertisement in the Advocate for shawls but the store is in Sturgeon Bay. Frank thought he could find someone who was going to Sturgeon Bay and would buy it for us. We know that Ma has been working on new suits for us. I guess she wants us all to have them for Christmas. Andrew Anderson is going to dress up like Santa for the Fish Creek school Christmas program next week and Miss Higgins arranged for me to borrow his outfit and play Santa at our school program tomorrow night. I don't know whether it's from turning thirteen or from going to a regular school or from getting a lot taller, but lately, it seems like people are treating me like I'm more grown up. Maybe I've been acting more grown up. Whatever the reason, I like the feeling.

Dec. 18 -- The school program turned out to be a lot of fun. The children all knew their parts real good and Ma said I did a good job as narrator. Then when I came out dressed up like Santa Claus, everyone clapped. The school board had a bag made up for each child with hard candy, nuts, a popcorn ball and an apple in it and my job as Santa was to pass out the bags. I think even the little ones figured out who Santa really was. There was a tree in the school all decorated with the paper chains and stars and such that we had been making the past few weeks. It only had a few candles on it and Miss Higgins made sure someone was in charge of watching the candles when they were lit. She said it wouldn't do to burn down our brand new school. Ma and Pa and Jim all came to the school program but Joe and Charlie went to the revival meeting put on by Pastor Greenfield at the Moravian Church in

Ephraim. I think they only went because Edith Gehrke and Gustie Spring were going to be there.

Dec. 19 -- We were talking about Ephraim today and how it came to be founded by a congregation of Moravians. The Moravian religion was started back in Europe long before Martin Luther came along. The local Moravians, led by Rev. Iverson, walked all the way up from Green Bay on the ice to found the village of Ephraim. The name means "doubly fruitful" in the Bible. They built their church right on the shore at first but later moved it up the hill with horses and pulleys. They decided that there would never be any taverns in Ephraim and that any painted buildings would be white. Moravian ladies sure are good cooks. Ma uses their recipe for Christmas cookies and she already has a batch mixed up. They are made with butter and molasses and spices and then the dough has to sit two weeks to ripen before it's rolled out real thin and cut into shapes. Ma makes Moravian sugar cake too. For that you put fresh mashed potatoes, not leftover ones, in a yeast dough and let it raise three times. Then you poke holes in the cake with your thumbs and fill the holes with butter and sugar. The Moravians have a special star with lots of points that they put up before Christmas. A few years back, Mrs. Valentine let Dr. Moss and his family stay with her for the summer and they've summered there every year since. What with other boarders as well, she has quite a hotel going now. There's others who have turned their homes into hotels, including Capt. Fordel Hogenson. He calls his place Evergreen Hotel and he winters the 57 foot trading schooner he built right there on the beach in front of the hotel. Pretty soon Ephraim will have as many summer visitors as Fish Creek.

SCOONER

Dec. 22 -- Today was probably the biggest day in my whole life. Being Sunday, a whole group of young folks including Gustie Larson skated out from Fish Creek to the lighthouse in the early afternoon. We had a good time pulling taffy, hanging greens, popping corn and stringing it, and singing Christmas songs around the piano. I played my guitar for Silent Night just like on the first night that song was ever played over in Austria. The sun had been out most of the day, and the weather was pretty warm for December. When it came time for everyone to go home, my brothers and I decided to strap on our skates too and skate part way back to Fish Creek with the group. We were out from Forsvold's aways when the ice broke through under Willie Hogan. He couldn't touch bottom and when he tried to pull himself up on the ice, it was so thin there that it just broke away under his weight. Everyone was afraid to go near him to help for fear they'd go through too. He was really freezing and it was starting to get dark. I got down on my belly and crawled out to Willie like a lizard until I could grab him real good around the wrists. Charlie crawled out behind me and grabbed hold of my feet and pulled and with others hanging onto Charlie, we were able to pull Willie out of the water and back toward shore to where the ice was safe. When it was all over, Gustie said I sure was brave and everyone treated me like I was a real hero. It felt pretty good. I went on home because I was wet and cold, but Jim and some of the others saw Willie home and he's going to be just fine. I know I'll never forget this day.

Dec. 25 -- Christmas Day, 1895. When I was a real little boy, I used to think that Santa Claus brought the Christmas tree when he came on Christmas Eve. When I would come downstairs on Christmas morning, there would be the tree in the parlor all decorated with celluloid ornaments, and strings of glass beads, and popcorn, and candles in metal holders, and little red and yellow candy cherries on wires. Now, of course, I get in on the fun of decorating it on Christmas Eve. I helped cut down the tree over at Shanty Bay earlier in the day. Pa's in charge of nailing the boards crosswise on the bottom so it won't tip over. Ma puts a bucket of water nearby just in case one of the candles starts the tree on fire. She makes sure at least one of us boys is in the parlor watching whenever the candles are lit. It sure is a real pretty sight. After the tree was up, we all went across the harbor to Ephraim for the Christmas Eve service in the Moravian church. Near the end of the service, everyone got to hold a burning beeswax candle with a red ribbon tied on it while we sang Silent Night. Ma liked the shawl we bought her a lot and sure enough, she had all our suits ready for us boys. Today we had a big holiday dinner like always with roast goose and ham and all the trimmings and we finished up with steamed cherry pudding with butter sauce. What with the rescue the other day and all, this has been my best Christmas ever.

Dec. 30 -- Ammie and Will got their names in the Advocate for participating in the Christmas night festivities at Baileys Harbor with seven or eight other Fish Creek boys. The paper also told about the death of Mrs. Levi Thorp of Egg Harbor. In an article about news of the year from around the world, I read that a German named Roetgen has invented a machine that uses some kind of rays to see inside your body and the Lumiere brothers in France are working on a machine that shows moving pictures. Mr. Gillette has made a razor that's supposed to be safer to use and Mr. Kellogg made grains of cereal into flakes. The Duryea brothers' horseless carriage won a race near Chicago against six other horseless carriages. The city hall in Milwaukee was finished after two years in the making and it is the third tallest building in the country. H.G.Wells wrote a book called The Time Machine that is causing quite a stir and some men in Pennsylvania are getting paid to play baseball for the entertainment of others. This will be my last entry in my journal, at least for this year. Ma said I did a real good job and it's up to me whether I want to continue in the new year. I'm not sure if I will or not, what with going to regular school and all. I'll be going to the New Year's Eve ball in Jorn's Hall over at Baileys Harbor tomorrow night. Gustie Larson will be there too so I might want to write about that come New Years Day. On January 25th there's going to be a grand masquerade ball in Fish Creek that my brothers organized and everyone is calling it the social event of the season. My brothers will be playing the violins and bass and I'll be playing my guitar. I just might want to write about that in my journal too. Maybe I'll start a new copy book and call it Eagle Bluff Journal 1896.

THE END

ANOTHER NOTE FROM THE AUTHOR: Walter Duclon lived in the Eagle Bluff Lighthouse and helped his father tend the light until several years after he married Gustie Larson. Then he and Gustie and their two children moved into their own home. They had two more children after that. Walter became an engineer on a tugboat that helped big ships get in and out of the port of Green Bay. Since 1926, when the Eagle Bluff light was made to turn on and off automatically, it hasn't been necessary for a lightkeeper to live in the lighthouse. Although the light itself was kept working and in good order, the house where the keeper had lived with his family was allowed to become rundown. When Walter was about eighty years old, the Door County Historical Society decided to restore the Eagle Bluff Lighthouse so it would be like it was when a lightkeeper and his family still lived there. Walter Duclon was a big help because he remembered what the lighthouse looked like when he was growing up in it. Although the old Fresnel lens is still in the lantern room on top of the tower, the light that the boats on Green Bay now use to guide them comes from a powerful flashing light that is outside the lantern room. The new light is solar powered, which means it gets the energy it needs to work from the sun. Visitors to Door County, Wisconsin can go inside the lighthouse in summer and fall.